## PIPE FITTINGS

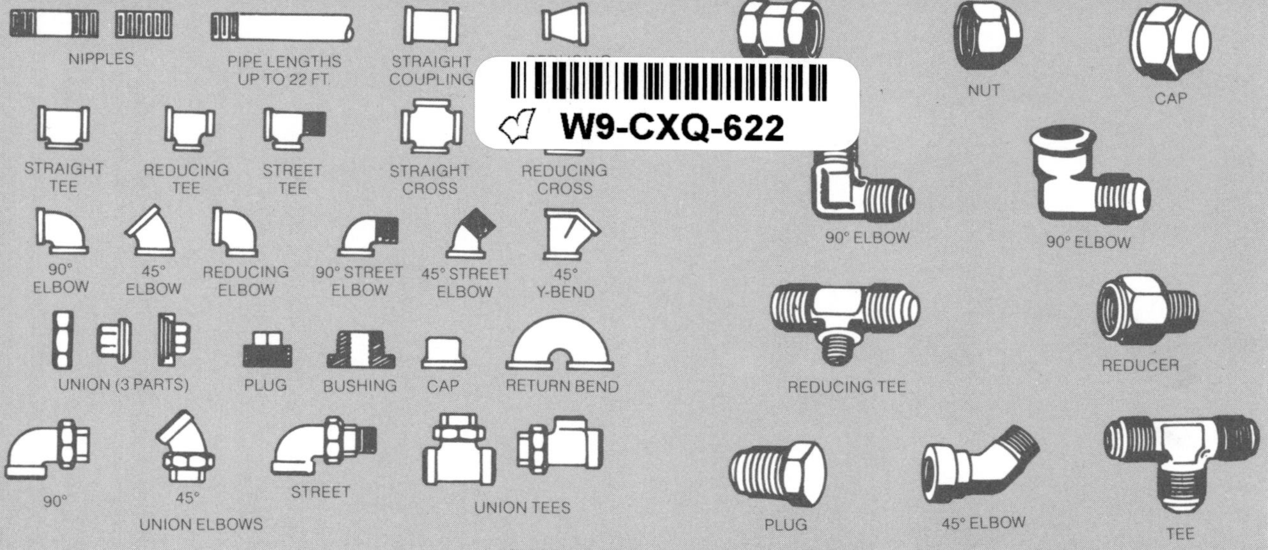

NIPPLES · PIPE LENGTHS UP TO 22 FT. · STRAIGHT COUPLING · NUT · CAP

STRAIGHT TEE · REDUCING TEE · STREET TEE · STRAIGHT CROSS · REDUCING CROSS · 90° ELBOW · 90° ELBOW

90° ELBOW · 45° ELBOW · REDUCING ELBOW · 90° STREET ELBOW · 45° STREET ELBOW · 45° Y-BEND · REDUCING TEE · REDUCER

UNION (3 PARTS) · PLUG · BUSHING · CAP · RETURN BEND

90° · 45° · STREET · UNION ELBOWS · UNION TEES · PLUG · 45° ELBOW · TEE

### MEASURES OF CAPACITY

- 1 cup = 8 fl oz
- 2 cups = 1 pint
- 2 pints = 1 quart
- 4 quarts = 1 gallon
- 2 gallons = 1 peck
- 4 pecks = 1 bushel

### STANDARD STEEL PIPE ((All Dimensions in inches)

| Nominal Size | Outside Diameter | Inside Diameter | Nominal Size | Outside Diameter | Inside Diameter |
|---|---|---|---|---|---|
| ⅛ | 0.405 | 0.269 | 1 | 1.315 | 1.049 |
| ¼ | 0.540 | 0.364 | 1¼ | 1.660 | 1.380 |
| ⅜ | 0.675 | 0.493 | 1½ | 1.900 | 1.610 |
| ½ | 0.840 | 0.622 | 2 | 2.375 | 2.067 |
| ¾ | 1.050 | 0.824 | 2½ | 2.875 | 2.469 |

## WOOD SCREWS

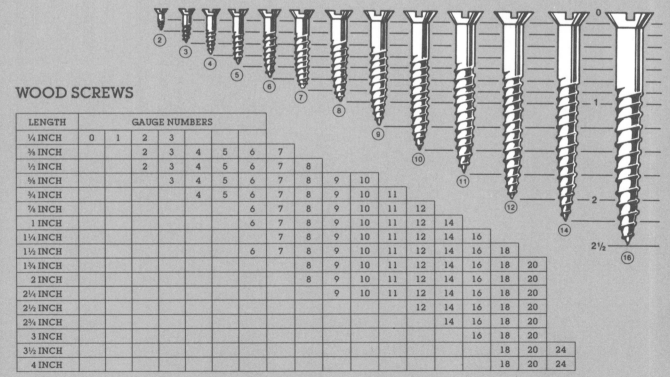

| LENGTH | GAUGE NUMBERS | | | | | | | | | | | | | |
|---|---|---|---|---|---|---|---|---|---|---|---|---|---|---|
| ¼ INCH | 0 | 1 | 2 | 3 | | | | | | | | | | |
| ⅜ INCH | | | 2 | 3 | 4 | 5 | 6 | 7 | | | | | | |
| ½ INCH | | | 2 | 3 | 4 | 5 | 6 | 7 | 8 | | | | | |
| ⅝ INCH | | | | 3 | 4 | 5 | 6 | 7 | 8 | 9 | 10 | | | |
| ¾ INCH | | | | | 4 | 5 | 6 | 7 | 8 | 9 | 10 | 11 | | |
| ⅞ INCH | | | | | | | 6 | 7 | 8 | 9 | 10 | 11 | 12 | |
| 1 INCH | | | | | | | 6 | 7 | 8 | 9 | 10 | 11 | 12 | 14 |
| 1¼ INCH | | | | | | | | 7 | 8 | 9 | 10 | 11 | 12 | 14 | 16 |
| 1½ INCH | | | | | | | 6 | 7 | 8 | 9 | 10 | 11 | 12 | 14 | 16 | 18 |
| 1¾ INCH | | | | | | | | | 8 | 9 | 10 | 11 | 12 | 14 | 16 | 18 | 20 |
| 2 INCH | | | | | | | | | 8 | 9 | 10 | 11 | 12 | 14 | 16 | 18 | 20 |
| 2¼ INCH | | | | | | | | | | 9 | 10 | 11 | 12 | 14 | 16 | 18 | 20 |
| 2½ INCH | | | | | | | | | | | | | 12 | 14 | 16 | 18 | 20 |
| 2¾ INCH | | | | | | | | | | | | | | 14 | 16 | 18 | 20 |
| 3 INCH | | | | | | | | | | | | | | | 16 | 18 | 20 |
| 3½ INCH | | | | | | | | | | | | | | | | 18 | 20 | 24 |
| 4 INCH | | | | | | | | | | | | | | | | 18 | 20 | 24 |

WHEN YOU BUY SCREWS, SPECIFY (1) LENGTH, (2) GAUGE NUMBER, (3) TYPE OF HEAD—FLAT, ROUND, OR OVAL, (4) MATERIAL—STEEL, BRASS, BRONZE, ETC., (5) FINISH—BRIGHT, STEEL BLUED, CADMIUM, NICKEL, OR CHROMIUM PLATED.

# Popular Mechanics

## do-it-yourself encyclopedia

The complete, illustrated home reference guide from the world's most authoritative source for today's how-to-do-it information.

# Volume 16

MEASUREMENTS

to

OUTDOOR FURNITURE

**HEARST DIRECT BOOKS**

NEW YORK

# Acknowledgements

The Popular Mechanics Encyclopedia is published with the consent and cooperation of POPULAR MECHANICS Magazine.

## For POPULAR MECHANICS Magazine:

Editor-in-Chief: *Joe Oldham*

Managing Editor: *Bill Hartford*

Special Features Editor: *Sheldon M. Gallager*

Automotive Editor: *Wade A. Hoyt, SAE*

Home and Shop Editor: *Steve Willson*

Electronics Editor: *Stephen A. Booth*

Boating, Outdoors and Travel Editor: *Timothy H. Cole*

Science Editor: *Dennis Eskow*

## Popular Mechanics Encyclopedia

Project Director: *Boyd Griffin*

Manufacturing: *Ron Schoenfeld*

Assistant Editors: *Cynthia W. Lockhart Peter McCann, Rosanna Petruccio*

Production Coordinator: *Peter McCann*

The staff of Popular Mechanics Encyclopedia is grateful to the following individuals and organizations:

Editor: *C. Edward Cavert*

Editor Emeritus: *Clifford B. Hicks*

Production: *Layla Productions*

Production Director: *Lori Stein*

Book Design: *The Bentwood Studio*

Art Director: *Jos. Trautwein*

Design Consultant: *Suzanne Bennett & Associates*

Illustrations: *AP Graphics, Evelyne Johnson Associates, Popular Mechanics Magazine, Vantage Art.*

**Contributing Writers:** Penelope Angell, *Aluminum-and-canvas chairs*, page 2038; John Burroughs, *Caliper selection and use*, page 1938; Walter E. Burton, *Setscrew chucks you can make*, page 1948; *Model this 24-pounder*, page 1968; Rosario Capotosto, *Measuring and marking*, page 1932; *Period moldings you can make*, page 1991; *Park bench furniture for your patio*, page 2032; Martin Cleeve, *Swing toolholder for your lathe*, page 1951; John F. Dryer, *Enlarge your micrometer*, page 1936; Sheldon M. Gallager, *Hideaway home theater*, page 2001; Ray M. Gates, *Sheet-metal brake you can make of wood*, page 1959; Jake Grubb, *Ship modeling: a challenge*, page 1974; R.S. Hedin, *Lathe boring-bar set*, page 1942; *Sheet-metal cutter that's easy to make*, page 1958; Glenn S. Hensley, *Riding mower selection*, page 2010; Len Hilts, *Home workshop motors repair*, page 1995; Russell James, *You're the rule*, page 1933; Charles J. Ksanda, *Lathe indexing attachment*, page 1947; W. Clyde Lammey, *Moldings—the finishing touch*, page 1982; Morton E. Milliken, *Shop forge you can build*, page 1960; Ed Nelson, *Measurements: an introduction*, page 1924; James R. Oswald, *Frame movies with a matte box*, page 1999; William Waggoner, *Piggyback speed reducer*, page 1998; C.W. Westrick, *Metal castings you can make yourself*, page 1964; Harry Wicks *Coffee table for your patio*, page 2017; Fred L. Wolff, *Scratch-built control-line airplanes*, page 1979; C.W. Woodson, *Sheet-metal know-how*, page 1952.

**Picture Credits:** Popular Mechanics Encyclopedia is grateful to the following for permission to reprint illustrations: Frank Caruso, pages 1924-1927.

ISBN 0-87851-169-5

Library of Congress 85-81760

10  9  8  7  6  5  4

PRINTED IN THE UNITED STATES OF AMERICA

Although every effort has been made to ensure the accuracy and completeness of the information in this book, Hearst Direct Books makes no guarantees, stated or implied, nor will they be liable in the event of misinterpretation or human error made by the reader, or for any typographical errors that may appear. WORK SAFELY WITH HAND TOOLS. WEAR SAFETY GOGGLES. READ MANUFACTURER'S INSTRUCTIONS AND WARNINGS FOR ALL PRODUCTS.

# Contents

# Measurements: an introduction

■ THROUGHOUT HISTORY people have required familiar, consistent and easily available units of measurement. The Biblical *cubit* was the length of the forearm from the elbow to the end of the middle finger (in ancient Egypt that amounted to approximately 20 of our modern inches). And consider the inch itself; our inch came from the early British measurement, which was defined as "the length of three barleycorns, round and dry."

### Forearms won't do

As people learned to master the environment and to build machines, such imprecise measurements no longer served them adequately. Neither forearms nor barleycorns are uniform, and no system of measurements is useful unless the units mean the same thing to all who use them. In fact, confusion in regard to exact meaning can lead to chaos.

Furthermore, the standard to be agreed upon must be available to all who use it. The distance from the tip of King Henry's nose to the end of his thumb—the official basis for the English *yard*—may have been totally consistent all the time the King was on his throne, but few Englishmen had access to it.

The length of the *mile* has been elastic, too.

**THE BIBLICAL CUBIT** came from the ancient Egyptian measure of the forearm from the elbow to the end of the middle finger. A do-it-yourself project 40 cubits high could vary greatly with individual craftsmen.

**THE OFFICIAL BASIS FOR THE ENGLISH YARD** was the distance from King Henry's nose to his Royal thumb. Only a few had access to this standard even during the time the King was on the throne.

Our word *mile* is a descendant of the Latin *milia passum,* or one thousand paces. The Roman *mile* had a very precise definition; it was one thousand paces measured from the point where the heel of one foot strikes the ground to the point where the same heel strikes the ground again. A precise definition all right, but a highly imprecise measurement. A Roman legionnaire built like Mickey Rooney would count off a good many more miles than one measuring up to Charlton Heston.

### Sailors and problems

*Nautical miles,* another oldtime measurement, have never had anything to do with paces. How can you walk on water? A *nautical mile* was defined as one minute of the Earth's circumference—1/21,600th of the way around the world. This, again, may appear to be a very precise measurement. And it *was* precise until it was discovered that the Earth isn't perfectly round, so a one-minute arc doesn't mean the same everywhere. As a result, the *nautical mile* has been redefined in feet; to be exact, a *nautical mile* measures 6076.1 feet.

Then along came aviation. Fliers use long-distance navigation methods developed by sea captains, but most early flying was done over land. As a result, U.S. aviators use both *statute* and *international nautical miles.* Sounds confusing? So adaptable is the human brain, however, that pilots and navigators quickly learn to convert, almost automatically, from one kind of mile to the other. No doubt aviators will be happy to settle, eventually, on the *kilometer.* However, this experience demonstrates how rapidly we can learn to shift from one measurement system to another, and do it without much difficulty when the need arises.

The metric system is a precisely defined body of weights and measures accepted by international authority.

It's quite correct to say that there have been several different metric systems, since some measurements have undergone a series of modifications. But for the most part these were only small refinements. Many of today's metric units aren't greatly different from the uniform units of measurement demanded by Talleyrand after the French Revolution.

Another name for metric units is "SI" units. That's the abbreviation bestowed on metrics by the General Conference on Weights and Measures, an international body that met for years to make revisions which for the most part were minuscule. Such revisions and simplifications finally were completed and accepted in 1960, and the entire body of measurements was named the *Systeme International d'Unites*. The conference decreed "SI" as the official abbreviation in all languages. (However, the U.S. Department of Commerce still prefers to call it the International Metric System.)

The metric system has had its share of ambiguities, too. In the 1700s the Paris Academy of Sciences throught it was pinning its basic unit of measurement—the meter—to one of nature's most constant realities; surveyors established the sea-level distance from the North Pole to the Equator, and the *meter* was defined as one 10-millionth of that length.

That, too, soon developed flaws. The average person trying to measure the distance from the North Pole to the Equator, and then fractionate it, was no more successful than the English serf who sought to measure the distance from King Henry's nose to the end of his Royal Thumb.

### Decimal convenience

Disregarding the Royal Thumb, the metric system offers one tremendous advantage over any other system ever invented. It's the same advantage that the United States coinage system had, until recently, over most other coinage systems since the early days of the Republic. This major advantage is *the decimal relationship of one unit to another*. If you can multiply by 10, or 100, or 1000, you can easily manipulate the system.

This is most helpful to those of us who desperately try to avoid multiplication and division. In the metric system, in most cases, a specific unit is 10 times the size of the next smaller unit, and 1/10th the size of the next larger unit.

Take the measurement of land, for example. (We ordinarily are accustomed to measuring in

**THE MILE IN ANCIENT ROME** was measured as the distance of 1000 paces. A twenty-mile hike in the Roman Legion would end with the troops scattered over a wide area, depending on the length of each Legionnaire's stride.

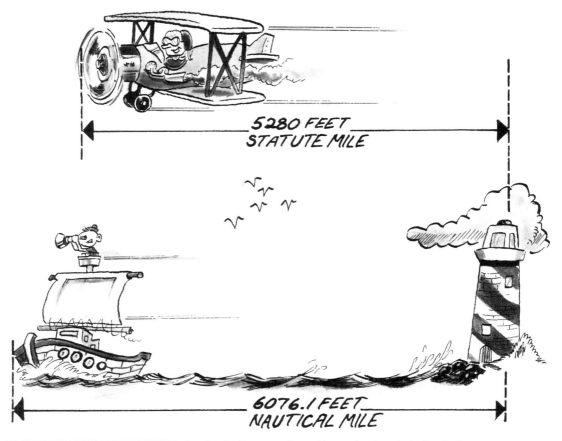

**PILOTS MUST CONVERT DISTANCE** in the air to both statute miles and international nautical miles. Both systems are used in aviation depending on the plane's altitude and ground control system.

*acres* or *square miles*—units which can have no logical relationship to one another.) In the metric system, the basic measurement of land area is the *are* (rhymes with bare). An *are* is defined as an area of land equivalent to a square measuring 10 meters on each side, or 100 square meters. A *hect-are* (*hecto-* is a prefix signifying 100) is 100 times the area of an *are*, or 10,000 square meters. The system obviously lends itself to rapid mental calculation. Thus an area of 235 *square meters* is equivalent to 2.35 *acres* and to .0235 hectare.

Compare that calculation with the arithmetic necessary to convert 4,367 square freet into square yards, square rods and acres!

Most other metric elements are just as regular in their decimal consistency. *Milli-* is the prefix for one one-thousandth, so a *milliliter* is a thousandth of a *liter*. This metric relationship is somewhat comparable to the number of cubic inches in a gallon in our customary system, except that there's no logic to our customary system. Well, how many cubic inches *are* there in a gallon? The answer is 231, but how many of us can be expected to know that, or even know how to compute it?

The relationship of cubic inches to gallons isn't the only example of our customary measuring units that fit together so clumsily they scarcely seem to fit at all.

### A foot is a foot?

Take something as familiar as the *foot*. No, the foot isn't always the same throughout the United States, and in our technological society even minor differences can be critical. In the U.S. there are two slightly different "approved" definitions for the *foot*, and the British offer still a third "approved" definition. The American Standards Association (now the American National Standards Institute) stated that a foot is precisely 0.3048 meter. The National Bureau of Standards says the foot is precisely 1200/3937 meter (which in decimals is about 0.3048006096).

Until deciding to go metric, the British, with

their usual aplomb, said the foot was precisely one-third of the Imperial *yard,* and then defined the *yard.* The result didn't match our own two clumsy feet.

The three different feet are close in size. Their relative lengths are in this ratio:

914,400:914,402:914,399

But why should there be any difference at all? Can't we all talk about a *foot*—or any other unit of measurement—and mean precisely the same thing?

### Whose quart counts?

Now take a look at the quart, which is one of the most familiar and comfortable old measurements we've known since we hit the refrigerator as kids. A *quart* measures volume, and it shouldn't matter whether that volume is filled with corn likker or corn flakes. So how much is a quart? A U.S. *liquid* quart is 57.75 cubic inches; our *dry* quart is 67.0062 cubic inches. There's a difference of 16 percent between the two.

In 1864 Great Britain, facing somewhat the same problem, consolidated a number of various-size quarts into one quart for all uses. It amounts to about 69.35 cubic inches—bigger than either of our quarts.

**AN ACCEPTABLE STANDARD** for a measurement must be constant and available to everyone. But even the force of gravity used to measure mass (weight) in pounds or kilograms is not constant.

### Ounces of turmoil

Now we plunge into an area of confusion. We have had a tendency in the past to use a single measuring unit for a variety of purposes. An *ounce,* for example, has been our unit for measuring troy weight, for measuring avoirdupois weight, and for measuring liquids. Yet these

**INTERNATIONAL ACCEPTANCE OF THE METRIC SYSTEM** has been much more widespread outside the U.S. Recent attempts by U.S. manufacturers to adopt the metric system resulted in double measurement labeling confusing the consumer and the do-it-yourselfer.

## HOW TO CONVERT TO—OR FROM—METRIC

Here are the factors to use in converting customary units to SI and *vice versa.* Most are approximate. To convert British nautical miles to meters, for example, a *precise* answer calls for you to multiply by 1853.184. But multiplying by 1850 would introduce an error of only about 17/100 of 1 percent. So our "approximate" factors still give you good, solid conversion figures.

This is how you use the table:

In starting with terms from the first column, multiply by the conversion factor in the second to find the equivalent in the SI units from the third column. Follow the arrows in the opposite direction to change from an SI quantity to its equivalent in customary units.

To make it easier to read long decimals, we follow the American National Standards Institute suggestion. We put digits in groups of three separated by spaces.

| Multiply→<br>To get← | →by→<br>←by← | →To get<br>←Multiply |
|---|---|---|

### ACCELERATION

| | | |
|---|---|---|
| feet per second<br>per second | →.304 8→<br>←3.281← | meters per second<br>per second |
| feet per second<br>per second | →.109 7→<br>←9.113← | kilometers per hour<br>per second |
| inches per second<br>per second | →.025 4→<br>←39.37← | meters per second<br>per second |
| miles per hour<br>per second | →1.609→<br>←.621 4← | kilometers per hour<br>per second |

### AREA

| | | |
|---|---|---|
| acres | →.4047→<br>←2.471← | hectares |
| square feet | →.092 9→<br>←10.76← | square meters |
| square inches | →6.452→<br>←.155 0← | square centimeters |
| square miles | →2.59→<br>←.386 1← | square kilometers |
| square yards | →.836 1→<br>←1.196← | square meters |

### FORCE

SI units use kilograms only as units of mass ("weight" in popular usage). Force has a basic SI unit of its own, the *newton,* based on the force of inertia, not the force of gravity. One newton is the force that, if applied to a free body of 1 kilogram mass, will accelerate it at a rate of 1 meter per second each second. A newton, in customary terms, equals about 3.7 ounces of force.

| | | |
|---|---|---|
| kilograms force | →9.807→<br>←.110 3← | newtons |
| ounces (avoirdupois) force | →.278 0→<br>←3.702← | newtons |
| pounds (avoirdupois) force | →4.448→<br>←.225 1← | newtons |

### ENERGY (including Work)

The *joule* is the SI unit of energy or work. It is the work done (or energy expended) when a 1-newton force displaces a body for 1 meter in the direction of the force.

| | | |
|---|---|---|
| British thermal units (mean) | →1055→<br>←.000 948 7← | joules |
| calories (mean) | →4.190→<br>←.238 7← | joules |
| ergs | →1 x $10^{-7}$→<br>←1,000,000← | joules |
| foot-pounds | →1.356→<br>←.738← | joules |
| kilowatt hours | →3,600,000→<br>←.000 000 277 8← | joules |

### LENGTH

| | | |
|---|---|---|
| caliber | →.025 4→<br>←39.37← | millimeters |
| chain (surveyor's)* | →20.12→<br>←.049 71← | meters |
| chain (engineer's)* | →30.48→<br>←.032 81← | meters |
| inches | →25.4→<br>←.039 37← | centimeters |
| mils (.001 inch) | →25.4→<br>←.039 37← | microns (.001 mm) |
| miles (U.S. nautical) | →1.852→<br>←.54← | kilometers |
| miles (U.S. statute) | →1.609→<br>←.621 4← | kilometers |
| rods | →5.029→<br>←.198 8← | meters |
| yards | →.914 4→<br>←1.094← | meters |

* A surveyor's chain, 66 feet, equals four 16½-foot rods or 100 7.92-inch links. An engineer's chain equals 100 12-inch links.

### MASS (Weight)

| | | |
|---|---|---|
| carats | →.2→<br>←5← | grams |
| grains | →.064 79→<br>←15.43← | grams |
| ounces (avoirdupois) | →28.35→<br>←.035 27← | grams |
| ounces (troy or apothecary) | →31.10→<br>←.032 15← | grams |
| pounds (avoirdupois) | →.453 6→<br>←2.205← | kilograms |
| short tons (2000 pounds) | →.907 2→<br>←.068 52← | kilograms |

### POWER

| | | |
|---|---|---|
| Btu (thermochemical) per hour | →.292 9→<br>←3.414← | watts |
| calories (thermochemical) per hour | →4.184→<br>←.239 0← | watts |
| ergs per second | →.000 000 1→<br>←10,000,000← | watts |
| foot-pounds (force) per second | →1.356→<br>←.737 6← | watts |

| | | |
|---|---|---|
| horsepower (550 foot-pounds per second) | →.745 7→ ←1.341← | kilowatts |

**PRESSURE**

The pascal (Pa), adopted as the special name for a unit of pressure, is a newton of force per square meter. (See Force for a discussion of the newton.)

| | | |
|---|---|---|
| atmospheres | →101,325→ ←.000 009 869← | pascals |
| kilograms per square centimeter | →66.5→ ←.000 010 2← | pascals |
| pounds per square foot | →47.88→ ←.020 89← | pascals |
| pounds per square inch | →6894.75→ ←.000 145← | pascals |

**SPEED**

| | | |
|---|---|---|
| feet per minute | →.005 08→ ←196.9← | meters per second |
| feet per second | →.304 8→ ←3.281← | meters per second |
| knots (international) | →1.852→ ←.539 96← | kilometers per hour |
| miles (U.S. statute) per hour | →1.609→ ←.621 4← | kilometers per hour |
| miles (U.S. statute) per minute | →94.41→ ←.010 59← | kilometers per hour |

**TORQUE**

| | | |
|---|---|---|
| ounce-inches | →.007 062→ ←141.6← | newton meters |
| pound-feet | →1.356→ ←.737 6← | newton meters |
| pound-inches | →.113→ ←8.851← | newton meters |

**VOLUME**

| | | |
|---|---|---|
| acre-feet | →1233.→ ←.000 810 7← | cubic meters |
| bushels (U.S.) | →.035 24→ ←28.38← | cubic meters |
| cords | →3.624 5→ ←.275 9← | cubic meters |
| cubic feet | →.028 32→ ←35.31← | cubic meters |
| cubic inches | →16.39→ ←.061 02← | cubic centimeters |
| cubic inches | →.016 39→ ←61.02← | liters |
| cubic yards | →.764 6→ ←1.308← | cubic meters |
| gallons (U.S. dry) | →4.405→ ←.227← | liters |
| gallons (U.S. liquid) | →3.785→ ←.226 4← | liters |
| ounces (U.S. fluid) | →29.57→ ←.033 81← | milliliters |
| ounces (U.S. fluid) | →.029 57→ ←33.81← | liters |
| pecks (U.S.) | →8.81→ ←.113 5← | liters |
| quarts (U.S. dry) | →1.101→ ←.908 1← | liters |
| quarts (U.S. dry) | →1101→ ←.000 908 1← | milliliters |
| quarts (U.S. liquid) | →.9464→ ←1.057← | liters |
| quarts (U.S. liquid) | →946.4→ ←.001 057← | milliliters |

measuring systems are basically incompatible. The units are called *ounces,* but they're far from equal. We have used *pounds* for weight, and *foot-pounds* for energy—a combination of terms born of our assumption that the force of gravity is uniformly constant. Confusion!

Since the force of gravity *isn't* uniformly constant, the two measuring systems really require different terms. The *kilogram* thus becomes the metric unit for measuring mass (scientists prefer the term "mass" to "weight"). And the *newton* thus becomes a unit for measuring force—the force needed to overcome inertia and accelerate a one-kilogram mass to a speed one meter per second in one second.

Regardless of how you feel about it, the wait for metrics has been a long one. Way back in 1821 John Quincy Adams told Congress that metrics offered "the ideal perfection of uniformity applied to weights and measures." But he added that the time wasn't yet ripe in the United States to adopt the decimal system. It has ripened very slowly.

### While we hung back

The rest of the world moved steadily toward metrics while we, clinging to our feet and yards, our ounces and pounds, our pints and gallons, were left alone among the great industrialized countries.

It seems almost inevitable that metrics eventually will become universal. But it's likely that in 1999 we'll still bet on horse races measured in furlongs, McDonald's may still be featuring a quarter-pounder rather than a 0.113398 kilogrammer, Erskine Caldwell's classic will not have been renamed *God's Little 0.4047 Hectare,* and the announcer at the Superbowl will not be saying, "First down and 9.144 meters to go."

# Guide to the right measurement

■ WHETHER YOU WANT to remodel your kitchen or add a room to your house, this guide can help you in the planning stage. It provides some basic measurements of common structures, equipment and material and recommended minimum dimensions. Widths are given as the narrower horizontal dimension or as the distance from left to right from the front of an item. Heights are given from the floor or from the bottom of suspended items. Depths are from front to rear. Some measurements are not given since they vary widely.

## DOORS

### FRAMING
Width and height of rough opening are 3½" larger than the door. Head and side casings are ½" x 1¾"; exterior door sill is 1⅝" x 7⅜"; a stock jamb with a ½" rabbet is 1⁵⁄₁₆" or 1⅝" x 5¼"

### ENTRANCE DOOR
Standardly 2'6", 2'8", 2'10" and 3' wide, and 6'8" and 7' high; thickness is 1¾"

### INTERIOR DOOR
Most commonly 2'4" and 2'6" wide; 6'6", 6'8" and 7' high; thickness is 1⅜" or 1¾"

### DOORBELL BUTTON
Commonly 45" above top of doorsill

### DOORKNOB
Commonly 36½" from floor

## STAIRS  Recommended stairway width 2'10"-3'

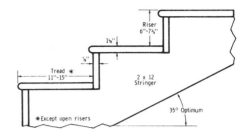

Outside stoop should be 4'6" deep to allow for storm door swing. Minimum step tread is 12" with ¼" pitch. Brick steps should be header fronted

## WINDOWS
Placement height is based on aligning with room door top. Measure distance from ceiling to door molding. Window sizes are widely variable. Common wood double-hung sizes: 2', 2'4", 2'8" and 3' wide; 3'2", 3'10" and 4'6" high

## RAILINGS
**STAIRCASE**—Height 2'10"-3'
**PORCH AND DECK**—Height 3'

## HOUSE WIRING
### MAJOR EQUIPMENT WATTAGE RATINGS

| | | | |
|---|---|---|---|
| Air conditioner 850-1200, 3100 | | Motor, ¼ hp. | 530 |
| Attic fan | 500-1500 | Oil burner | 300-550 |
| Clothes dryer | to 4500 | Range | 7000-14,000 |
| Dishwasher | 530-1000 | Refrigerator | 200-670 |
| Disposer | 380-530 | Television | 200-400 |
| Furnace blower | 380-670 | Toaster | 600-1350 |
| Heater | 1000-1650 | Washer, automatic | 350-900 |
| Home freezer | 300-670 | Water heater | 750-3000 |

## ROOMS—MINIMUM SIZE RECOMMENDATIONS

| | WIDTH | LENGTH | HEIGHT THICKNESS | DEPTH |
|---|---|---|---|---|
| **KITCHEN,** for 4 persons, depends on layout and equipment | 7' | 10' | | |
| **BATHROOM** | 5' | 7' | | |
| **DINING ROOM** with 36" chair room | 10' | 10' | | |
| **BEDROOM,** including 8' of clothing drawer space per person: | | | | |
| Single bed | 8' | 12' | or 10'x10' | |
| Double bed | 12' | 13' | or 10'x15' | |
| Twin beds | 12' | 15'6" | or 10'x17'6" | |
| **GARAGE** without laundry or shop: | | | | |
| One car with 8' or 9' door | 12' | 22' | | |
| Two-car with 2-8' or 16' door | 19' | 22' | | |
| Storage above car hood | | | 4' | 5' |
| Workbench on side, add to width | 3'6" | 36" | | |
| Floor should pitch toward door ⅛" per foot | | | | |

## FURNISHINGS & APPLIANCE RECOMMENDATIONS

| KITCHEN | WIDTH | LENGTH | HEIGHT THICKNESS | DEPTH | CLEARANCE |
|---|---|---|---|---|---|
| Base Cabinet (undersink and corners not included in frontage; height includes counter top) | 6'-10' | | 36" | 22"-25" | |
| Common individual widths: 12", 15", 18", 21", 24", 27", 30", 36", 42", 48" | | | | | |
| Wall cabinet—for 4 persons | 6'-10' | | { 12" 13" 14" | | |
| —for service for 12 | 10'-14' | | | | |
| Common individual widths: 15", 18", 21", 24", 27" 30", 33", 36", and 44"-60" (triple units) | | | | | |
| Common heights: 15", 18", 21", 24", 30", 31". Top shelf maximum height from floor is 6' | | | | | |
| Cabinet placed above range | | | | 30" | |
| above sink | | | | 22" | |
| above counter | | | | 15"-18" | |
| Counter space needed (not including corners; may be reduced by multiple use) | | | | | |

| | WIDTH | LENGTH | HEIGHT THICKNESS | DEPTH | CLEARANCE |
|---|---|---|---|---|---|
| next to: Refrigerator | 15″-18″ | | | | |
| Sink, each side | 18″ | | | | |
| Food preparation, mixing | 36″ | | | | |
| Range | 15″ | | | | |
| Oven | 15″ | | | | |
| Wall oven—Open door should be 3″-5″ below elbow. Average height from floor to bottom of oven is 27″-32″ | | | | | |
| Common kitchen appliance sizes: | | | | | |
| Refrigerator | 36″ | | 59″ | | |
| 1-bowl sink | 24″ | | | | |
| 2-bowl sink | 36″ | | | | |
| Range | 30″ | | 36″ | | |
| Built-in range | 30″ | | | | |
| Built-in oven | 24″ | | | | |
| Dishwasher | 24″ | | 34½″-36″ | | |
| **DINING AREA** | | | | | |
| Dining table, allow 2′ per person | 30″-42″ | | 30″ | | 36″ / 20″ knee |
| 8 persons fit at a 5′ round, a 4′ square or a 3′x8′ rectangle | | | | | |
| Dining counter | | | 36″ | | |
| Barstool (footrest 6″-8″ from floor) | | | 24″-25″ | | 12″ knee |
| Wainscoting | | | 30″ | | |
| **BATHROOM** | | | | | |
| Sinks | | | 31″-36′ | | |
| Tubs, square & square corner | 3′10″, 4′1½″ | | | | |
| Tubs, rectangular | 2′6″-2′9″ | 4′-5′6″ | | | |
| Free-standing shower cabinet, square and corner | 2′6″-3′6″ | 6′3″-7′ | | | |
| Toilets | 17¾″-29¼″ | | | 26″-31⅜″ | 18″ front |
| Shower head | | | 74″ | | |
| Curtain rod for tub | | | 78″ | | |
| Towel bar | | | 36″-42″ | | |
| Medicine cabinet from floor | | | 48″-54″ | | |
| Tiling (4¼″x4¼″)—room walls, plus trim | | | 10 tiles | | |
| —tub area from floor, plus trim | | | 16 tiles | | |
| **BEDROOM** | | | | | |
| Double bed (inside frame measure) | 54″ | 75″, 78″ | | | |
| Twin bed (inside frame measure) | 39″ | 75″, 78″ | | | |
| Clothes closet (depth is minimum) | | | 7′-7′6″ | 22″ | |
| Closet rod | | | 5′3″ | | |
| Chest of drawers | 36″ up | | 28″-34″ | 18″-21″ | |
| **WORK AREAS** | | | | | |
| Laundry area space in front of washer and dryer | 66″ | | | 36″ | |
| Space for hand ironing | 72″ | | | 52″ | |
| Bookshelves and cases (adjustable shelves have pin holes 1″ o.c.) | | | 6′6″ to top shelf | 8″-9″ | |

## MATERIALS

### BOARD & LUMBER SIZES

Nominal & actual dimensions: 1x2=¾″x1⅝″, 1x3=¾″x2⅝″, 1x4=¾″x3⅝″, 1x5=¾″x4⅝″, 1x6=¾″x5½″, 1x8=¾″x7½″, 1x10=¾″x9½″, 1x12=¾″x11½″; 2x4=1⅝″x3⅝″, 2x6=1⅝″x5⅝″, 2x8=1⅝″x7½″, 2x10=1⅝″x9½″, 2x12=1⅝″x11½″

### SHEET MATERIALS

Interior plywood—Most common sizes: 4′x8′, 4′x10′ and 4′x12′; also available, widths 30″-48″, lengths 5′-12′, thicknesses 3/16″ and ¼″-¾″ by eighths

Exterior plywood—Same dimensions as interior except in thicknesses: 3/16″ and ¼″-1⅛″ by eighths

Gypsum wallboard—Width 4′, lengths 4′ and 8′, thicknesses ¼″-⅝″ by eighths

Asbestos cement wallboard—Width 4′, lengths 4′ and 8′, thicknesses ⅛″ and 3/16″

Fiber wallboard—Standard width 4′, lengths 4′-12′, thicknesses ⅜″-¾″ by eighths. Also 4′x14′ & 16′, 8′x14′ & 16′ and 8′x18′

Hardboard, standard & tempered—Widths 2′, 4′ and 5′; lengths 2′-16′; thicknesses ⅛″-5/16″ by sixteenths

Plastic laminate—Widths 24″, 30″, 36″, 48″; lengths 60″, 72″, 84″, 96″, 120″, not all combinations; thickness 1/16″

### MASONRY

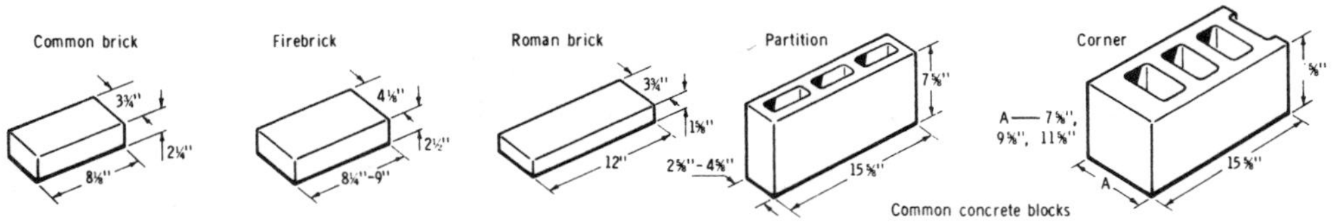
Common brick
3¾''
2¼''
8⅛''
Firebrick
4⅛''
2½''
8¼''-9''
Roman brick
3¾''
1⅝''
12''
Partition
7⅝''
2⅝''-4⅝''
15⅝''
Corner
A—7⅝'',
9⅝'', 11⅝''
15⅝''
A
Common concrete blocks

Concrete—General-purpose mix is 1:2¼:3. To make 1 cu. yd., use 6¼ sacks of cement, 14 cu. ft. of sand, 20 cu. ft. of gravel and 6 gal. of water per bag of cement

**INSULATION**—Commonly available are rolls and loose insulation. Rolls are 16″ o.c. x 36′; loose comes in 4-cu.-ft. bags; also 16″ and 24″ o.c. 4′ batts and 8′ blankets (o.c.=on center)

**GUTTERS**—4″ and 5″ wide, 10′ long; add connectors, corners and leader adapters to measure length; minimum slope is 1/16″ per foot

# Measuring and marking

**MOST COMMON TOOLS** for measuring and marking: 1, bench rule; 2, metal yardstick; 3, folding extension rule; 4, steel tape measure; 5, caliper rule; 6, combination square; 7, trammel points; 8, protractor; 9, T-bevel; 10, utility knife; 11, awl; 12, dividers.

■ ACCURACY IN MEASURING and marking is mostly a matter of using the right tool in the proper manner. The most common choices of marking and measuring tools are the ones you see here. When using any of these tools, be conscious of your angle of view, or you may err because of the parallax effect. This is the apparent displacement of two points (the desired point on the rule and the corresponding point you want to make on the workpiece) caused by different angles of view. This is why some rules have graduation marks on a bevel that runs down as close to the work surface as possible. Most sturdy metal rules don't have bevels, so turn these rules on edge to bring the graduation mark closer to the work surface.

To make your mark, use a medium-hard lead such as 2H. This produces a thin line that is much easier to work with than a bold, irregular line.

The way you hold most tools is also very important. Hold a pencil at about 80° to the work surface so the point rides in the corner formed by the rule edge and the work.

When marking a line with a square or T-bevel, place the pencil point on the measured mark and slide the other tool up to it.

Use a compass or trammel points to mark out circles or curved lines. Measure diameters with a caliper rule. Use a protractor for angles.

**HOLD A THICK RULE ON EDGE** to strike off a measurement for greatest accuracy. Distortion from viewing angle is minimized.

**HOLD YOUR PENCIL** so the lead point rides in the corner. Always use medium-hard lead pencils and keep the points sharp.

**AVOID STRIKING WIDE LINES** (left). These are usually caused by soft dull leads. A good lead to use is rated 2H (right).

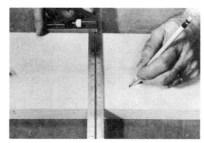

**HOLD THE PENCIL POINT** on the measured mark and carefully slide the square up to the point. Then strike your line.

**MARKING DOVETAILS** with a utility knife gives you greater accuracy than a pencil. Score also aids in beginning cutting work.

**USE THE CALIPER RULE** to measure diameters or thickness of stock. The stepped jaw projects are for inside measuring.

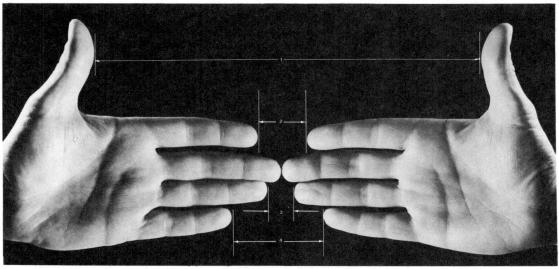

**WITH MIDDLE FINGERS** touching and thumbs stretched, measure 1, 2, 3 and 4 for your hands.

# You're the rule

■ WHAT DO YOU DO when you need a quick measurement, but don't have a ruler handy? What if close is good enough, but the consequences of eyeball measurement are less than appealing? Here's a solution: Take the time to "calculate" some of the handiest measurements around—those of your own body.

You can start with your hands. Place them over a ruler (palms up, thumbs stretched, middle fingers touching) and note the dimensions between all opposing fingertips (see 1 through 4).

In examples 5, 6 and 7, use your little finger as a stop and record measurements from the edge of a board to each tip; also the difference between tips. This works just as well if you place your hand flat. Simply catch the fingernail of your little finger below the edge of what you're measuring.

A similar principle operates for Nos. 8 and 9. The middle finger is the stop and by changing knuckles you get two quick reference points. Of course, dimensions on "biophysical rulers" vary depending on the individual. So experiment— find those most valuable to you. With practice, you can be accurate within ¹⁄₁₆ in. with no trouble.

Your palm also provides valuable measure-

ments, such as those obtained from the creases between finger joints. Even when rulers are available, you may find that your fingers are quicker. Make pencil marks on knuckles for those few increments you don't have "on hand."

Larger measurements are also available. The length of your outstretched arm from armpit (or tip of nose) to your middle fingertip is particularly useful, as is the distance between tips when both arms are stretched wide.

Other horizontal measurements come from

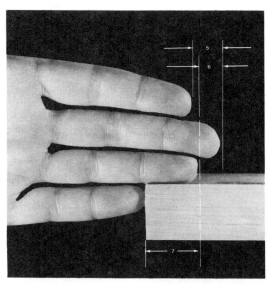

**BUTT YOUR** little finger to an edge and make three more measurements (see the text).

**BY PLACING** fingers as shown you'll have a "protractor" with 60° angle and perpendicular line.

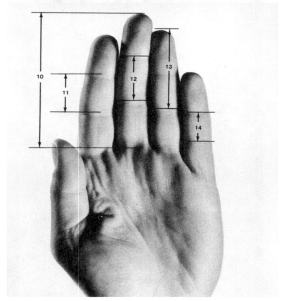

**AT LEAST** five dimensions are available by simply placing your hand down, palm up.

holding one or both elbows out to your side with your hands on your waist. When both elbows are spread, you can quickly approximate the width of such things as doorways and save the headache of trying to move something big through too small an opening.

For vertical measurements, try the distance between the floor and the tip of your nose, and don't forget to make an adjustment when you change your shoes. The same notion applies to the distance from the floor to your belt buckle or chin.

The possibilities are limitless. Even diameters can be judged with your personal ruler. The difference between tubing sizes can be readily determined depending on which knuckle the tubing jams on when slid over the finger. For example, ½-in. tubing may jam on the first knuckle of your little finger, ⅝ in. on the second knuckle and ¾ in. may clear both.

Larger outside diameters can be known by the combination of thumb and finger that will most nearly encircle them. For still larger diameters, both hands together could supply a ballpark figure.

You can use your hands for close approximations of often used angles (No. 15). Make a triangle of your fingers as pictured and press it against a table edge. The line that intersects where both fingertips and knuckles meet is perpendicular to the edge of the table, thus giving a 90° angle that is surprisingly accurate. In the process, an equilateral triangle is formed, giving the 60° angles shown.

Finally, by making the old V for victory sign with your middle and first fingers, you get a 45° angle. Of course, these angles and some other measurements mentioned might be something that you'd never use. But, unlike your tape measure, they will always be with you.

**MAKE** a "gun" of one hand, using the forefinger as the barrel. Fold your middle finger at the third knuckle (left) and then at the second (below). On the hand shown we got 3¼ in. and 1½ in., respectively.

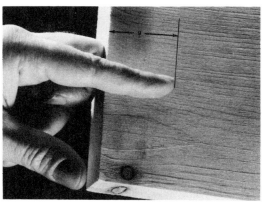

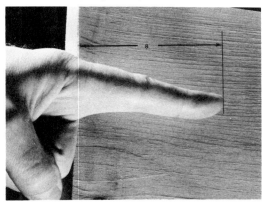

# Framing square basics

■ A FRAMING SQUARE is an indispensable tool if you're doing rough carpentry. It holds a wealth of pertinent information on its body—the 2-in.-wide leg—and its tongue—the 1½-in.-wide leg. Fortunately, most squares are sold with an instruction booklet that explains how to use the tool fully.

To understand how a square works, you must first understand that roof pitch is described as a ratio of rise to run, that is, how much the roof moves up in elevation for every foot it moves over in span. Sometimes the pitch is represented as a fraction like 4/12 (4 in. of rise for each 12 in. of run) or as a rise number, namely 4.

By placing the square on the rafter stock as shown, with the pitch number on the tongue and the 12-in. mark on the body both intersecting the same board edge, the proper pitch angle is automatically found. Then by reading below the pitch number on the body, the table gives the rafter length per foot of rafter run. In the case of a typical gable roof, you divide the overall span of the building from the outside edge of the front and back walls by two. Then take this figure and multiply it by the number found on the table. This is the rafter length from the *center of the ridge* to the outside of the wall plates. To establish the exact length, deduct half the ridge thickness and add the overhang width.

**1** Place square on face of rafter stock so pitch number on tongue and 12-in. mark on body meet board edge.

**2** Deduct half of ridge thickness from rafter length by moving square down edge ¾ in. Maintain alignment of marks.

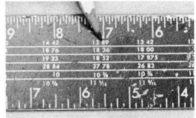

**3** To determine rafter length, find multiplier located under pitch number on line *LENGTH OF COMMON RAFTERS*.

**4** Multiply number from table by one-half building's span to find rafter length. Measure from plumb line *not* cut line.

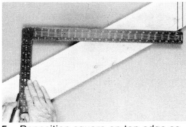

**5** Reposition square on top edge so angle is the same as before *and* so tongue intersects rafter length mark

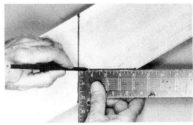

**6** Hold square body perpendicular to lower plumb line and move up until 4-in. mark intersects bottom edge of rafter.

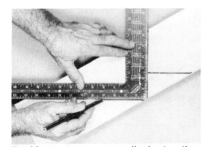

**7** Move square perpendicular to other side of plumb line, with corner at bottom edge. Mark desired width of rafter tail.

**8** Reposition square so proper marks again meet top edge of board *and* so the tongue intersects end of tail width line.

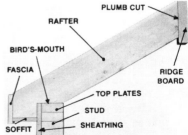

**9** Cut rafter shows proper fit of all components. Bird's mouth must sit flat on wall plate and plumb cut must be tight to ridge.

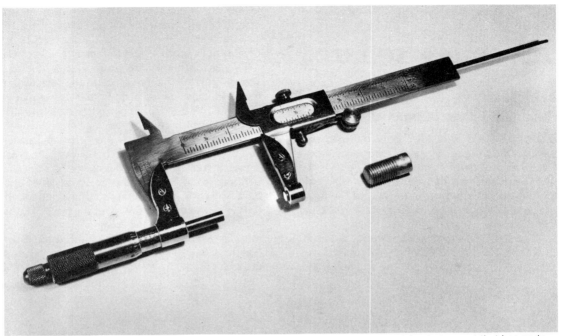

**IF YOU BUILD** this hybrid tool, you can turn your small 1-in. micrometer into a precision instrument that has up to four times its original capacity.

# Enlarge your micrometer

■ COMBINE A VERNIER CALIPER with a micrometer and increase the accuracy of the former and the capacity of the latter. This hybrid, accurate to .001 in., eliminates the need for a larger, more expensive micrometer. This enlarged micrometer is made with a 1-in. micrometer and 5-in. caliper, but select the size combinations that best suit your requirements.

Begin by opening the caliper jaws slightly to align the micrometer as shown. Then clamp the micrometer tightly to the caliper jaws and drill four holes through both tools using a No. 50 bit. For calipers with surface-hardened steel, use a small, high-speed grinding tool to penetrate the surface. A good bit will then drill into it. If the bit doesn't deliver chips, grind more. Tap threads in the caliper holes for No. 2-56 machine screws and enlarge micrometer holes with a No. 43 bit to accommodate the screws. Use a hacksaw to cut out the middle section of the micrometer. Screw the remaining anvil and spindle ends to the caliper as shown.

To measure, set the micrometer's handle gauge at 0 and slide the caliper jaw to bring the anvil snugly against the spindle. On our prototype, the jaw stops at 1-7/32 in. At this "standard" setting, lengths from 0 to 1 in. are measured by placing the work between the anvil and spindle of the micrometer and adjusting the micrometer gauge to obtain a reading. For larger measurements, slide caliper jaw in 1-in. increments away from spindle (e.g. to measure between 2 and 3 in. with micrometer, set caliper at 2-7/32 in.; between 3 and 4 in., set caliper at 3-7/32 in., and so on).

Apply the same pressure on all readings to insure accuracy. Using a larger caliper increases the range of the micrometer. However, accuracy will be no better than the finest unit on the micrometer gauge.

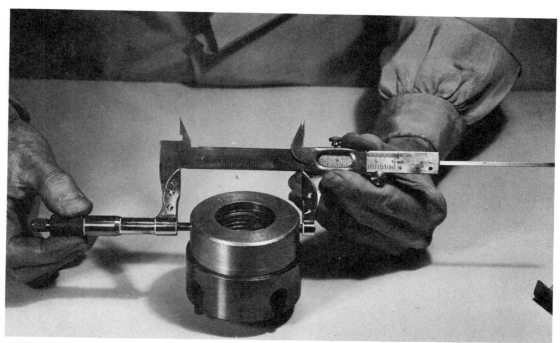

**NEW TOOL** measures lengths up to 4¼ in. using a 5-in. vernier caliper. You may want to remove the depth gauge tongue seen projecting at the right on the caliper.

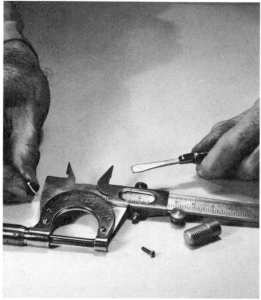

**FOR ACCURATE** alignment, drill holes and fasten micrometer to the caliper jaws to test fit before cutting off the middle section of the micrometer frame.

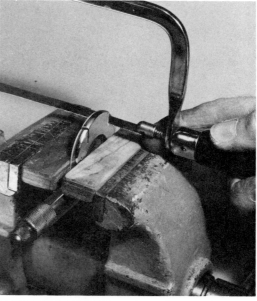

**CLAMP MICROMETER** in a vise and cut out the middle section. When assembling, align anvil and spindle accurately as if frame still connected them.

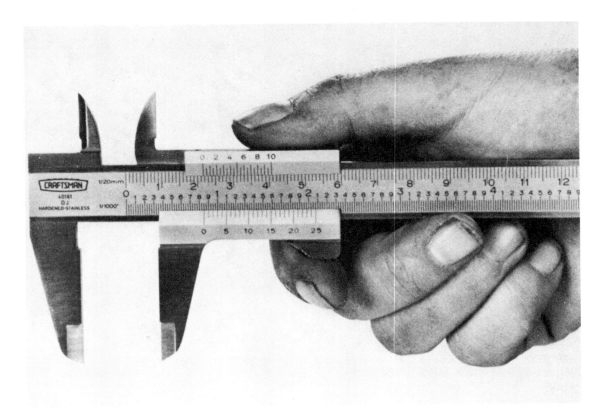

# Caliper selection and use

■ ALTHOUGH MACHINISTS have used them for years, precision vernier calipers have until recently been far too expensive to be known as popular home workshop tools. But now there's a new class of vernier calipers that is appearing on the commercial market— serviceable 6-in. precision calipers that are competitively priced.

These relatively inexpensive calipers are universal pattern models with scissors-like inside jaws integral with the outside jaws. They are beautifully finished instruments—hardened stainless steel throughout, with nicely fitted slides, accurately lapped jaws and legible satin-chromed photoengraved scales.

The photoengraved scales account for the tools' relatively low prices. Best-quality 6-in. vernier calipers have machine-divided scales engraved on pantograph engraving machines. Photoengraved scales are made by a process similar to that used to make printing plates; that is, they're printed from glass master negatives and then etched. While the etched graduations aren't quite as crisp as the machine-cut graduations, you'd need a magnifying glass to tell the difference. Indeed, for general shopwork a photoengraved caliper is completely satisfactory.

Actually it's about the handiest pocketsized measuring tool imaginable for home workshop wood and metalworking. When you want a precision measurement, you can use the caliper's vernier to get a reading within a thousandth of an inch. When gnat-whisker accuracy isn't really required—when you're measuring the thickness of lumber, for example—you can forget the vernier and use the tool as a plain slide caliper.

A precision reading takes a little mental arithmetic, but this soon becomes second nature. All verniers are alike in principle. They're simply auxiliary scales used to subdivide the smallest graduations on the caliper bar's scale into as many parts as there are graduations on the vernier. Thus, you could consider a vernier as just a system of offsets.

### *How to use the vernier*

*The 25-division verniers used with the decimal-inch scales are 25 thousandths of an inch shorter in total length than the equivalent graduations on the bar scale.* This means that with the caliper closed, the vernier's zero-line is aligned with the bar's zero-line, but the vernier's first graduation is offset one thousandth from its corresponding line on the scale above; the second graduation is offset two thousandths; the third three thousandths; and so on.

With the caliper opened, the vernier zero-line indicates the measurement to be read. Thus, to read the bar scale, first note the number of whole inches (to the left of this line), then add the tenths

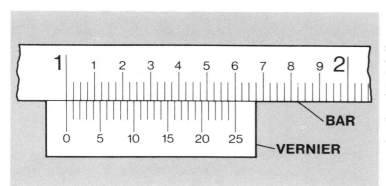

**SHORT** 25-division scale often found on older types of calipers is seldom used on newer models. The bar's scale is divided into tenths of inches, with each tenth divided into four parts or fortieths. The vernier subdivides these 1/40-in. graduations into 25 parts, each part being a thousandth.

**LONG** 25-division vernier found on most of the new calipers is similar to short vernier, but the vernier graduations are double-spaced to make it easier to take accurate measurements. On the thousandths vernier, the reading is .317 in. The top vernier, indicating millimeters, divides metric scale's millimeter into twenty parts. Can you make the equivalent reading in millimeters?

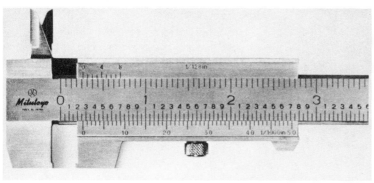

**EXTRA-LONG** 50-division vernier is featured on some newer makes of calipers. The bar scale has numbered tenths, each of which is divided into two parts, or twentieths. The vernier subdivides these 1/20th graduations into 50 parts, or thousandths. The reading shown is .265 inches. The top vernier scale divides the fractional-inch scale divisions (1/16ths) into eight parts or 1/128ths. What is equivalent fractional reading?

**CALIPERS ORDINARILY** are accurate to within one thousandth, more than sufficient for most work.

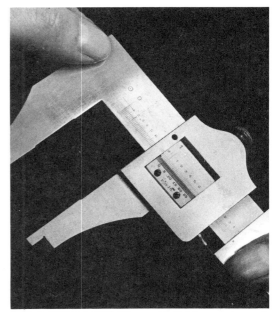

**OLDER STYLE CALIPERS** have 25-division verniers only .6 inches long, require use of a magnifying glass.

**TO MEASURE DIAMETERS** hold caliper square with work, take more than one reading for minimal error.

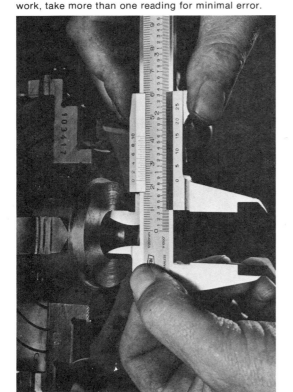

of an inch, which are numbered. Next, count the smallest graduations, which are fortieths of an inch, or 25 thousandths each, and add them. Finally, using the vernier, measure and add any fraction of a small graduation remaining.

*Measuring this extra fraction* is simply a matter of running your eye along the vernier scale to see which graduation matches a graduation of the bar scale. For example, if the vernier's 17th line matches a line above, the vernier's zero-line is offset 17/25ths of a graduation, or 17 thousandths past the last graduation on the bar scale.

Simply stated, if you think in terms of "whole inches plus 100-thousandths plus 25 thousandths plus thousandths," it's easy to quickly make any reading in thousandths mentally.

### Special features

Universal-pattern vernier calipers have two bar scales, upper and lower. The decimal-inch scale (inches graduated in tenths) is the more frequently used. The other scale may be either metric (centimeters and millimeters) or ordinary fractional-inch (inches graduated in sixteenths).

**DEPTHS CAN BE MEASURED** with the sliding jaw or rod on end of caliper beam. Vernier indicates reading.

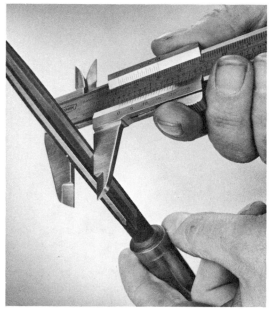

**USE SPECIAL CARE** when measuring hardened-steel cutting tools to prevent damage to caliper's jaws.

**CALIPER JAWS** are lapped until exactly parallel, so they can be used to check if work planes are parallel.

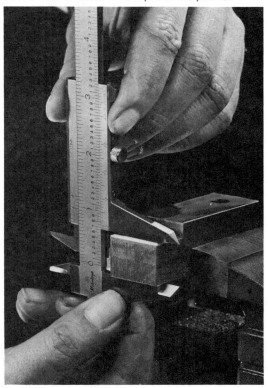

A metric scale's vernier subdivides the bar scale's millimeters into twentieths or fiftieths. A fractional-inch scale's vernier subdivides the bar scale's sixteenths into eight parts, or 128ths of an inch. On most calipers the two scales have a common zero-line, which permits reading equivalents—thousandths of an inch to millimeters, for example.

The slides of some 6-in. models have thumbscrew locks, while others have thumb-released friction locks. Some tools have fixed vernier plates—others have plates that can be adjusted to compensate for jaw wear. There are models with carbide-tipped jaws or fine-adjusting microscrews.

While a micro-screw caliper is considered preferable for machinework, a tool with a friction lock is more convenient for home workshop use.

No matter which model you choose, preserve your caliper's precision by taking care not to mar or spring its jaws. Also wipe the bar often with a lightly oiled rag to prevent grit or metal chips from working under the slide.

# Lathe boring-bar set

**FINISHED SET** nestles in hardwood stand with spare boring-bar blanks and Allen wrench.

■ EVERY OWNER of a metal-turning lathe should have a boring-bar set to increase its machining capability. This set has features that make it especially useful: It will bore a large range of hole diameters, and the holder is made so that bars can be rotated to set the rake angle, while a separate adjustment sets the tool to the spindle center.

The holder is made from ½-in.-square stock. The shank is of two pieces, welded or screwed together. Depending on the lathe used, it may be necessary to adjust the location of part B on part A so bits can be adjusted for center; the prototype was made for a 10-in.-swing lathe. Part C has a reamed hole to fit the boring bars' shanks; saw the clamping slot after reaming the hole. The washer for the capscrew that holds part C to part B was made thick so it would not be deformed in use.

**UPPER SCREW** on toolholder clamps the boring bar. The lower screw clamps vertical adjustment to set the cutting edge on center.

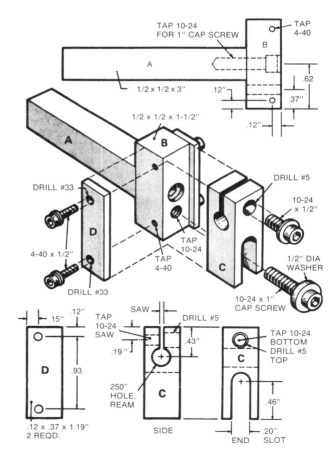

The boring bars are made from .250-in.-dia. water-hardening drill rod. Two styles are shown; forged and turned. Bars for boring large holes are heated and bent to form an offset. To bend the offset on a boring-bar blank, heat the end until it is bright red, then insert it into a hole drilled into a scrap steel plate, and bend the blank over; two torches may be necessary to get enough heat. The offset is then ground or filed to shape the cutting edge.

Small-hole bars are made by turning the shank down and leaving a knob on the end, then grinding or filing to form the cutting edge. These bars can be used to bore holes as small as .20-in. dia.

Harden the cutting end of each blank by heat-ing it to a bright-red color and quenching it in water to which a little table salt has been added to prevent soft spots. Remove surface discoloration with abrasive cloth, and draw the hardened end by heating the bar with a low flame until the end is a light straw color, then quench again in water. Apply heat about ¾ in. from the end and watch the color crawl to the cutting edge. Overheating (to a dark straw or blue color) will make the edge too soft.

After hardening and drawing the end, grind the cutting edge and hone it with an oilstone. Because this is carbon steel and not alloy steel, the bars will not take high heat—so use low speeds and feeds when machining with them.

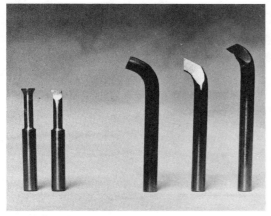

**BLANKS AND** their finished boring bars: Above, left: turned blank and bit made from it. Above, right: forged blank and bit; bit at right is threading tool.

**TOOLHOLDER HAS** a 3-inch shank that allows it to be clamped firmly into the toolpost.

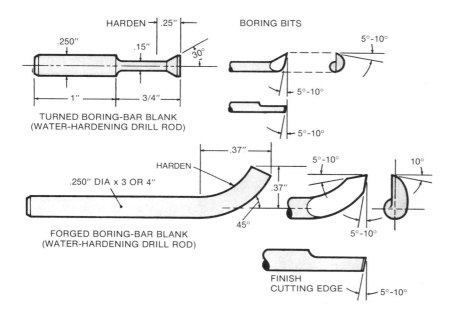

HARDEN .25"
.250"
.15"
30°
1"
3/4"
TURNED BORING-BAR BLANK
(WATER-HARDENING DRILL ROD)

BORING BITS
5°-10°
5°-10°
5°-10°

HARDEN
.250" DIA x 3 OR 4"
.37"
.37"
45°
FORGED BORING-BAR BLANK
(WATER-HARDENING DRILL ROD)
5°-10°
5°-10°
10°
5°-10°

FINISH CUTTING EDGE
5°-10°

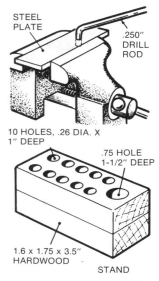

STEEL PLATE
.250" DRILL ROD
10 HOLES, .26 DIA. X 1" DEEP
.75 HOLE 1-1/2" DEEP
1.6 x 1.75 x 3.5" HARDWOOD
STAND

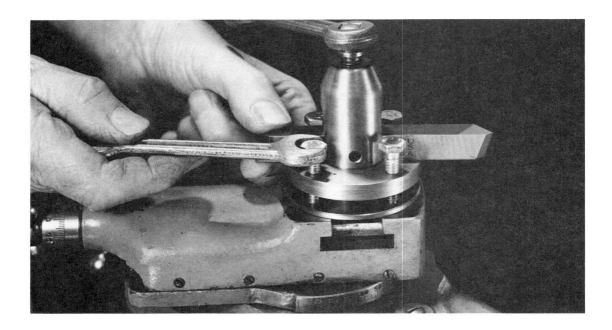

# King-size toolpost

**THE OVERSIZE POST** starts as a 1⅛-in. rod. The bottom hole is drilled and tapped for a mounting stud.

**THE TOP HOLE** should be drilled and tapped for a ⅜-16 clamping bolt, preferably with a square head.

■ HEFTY, HIGH-SPEED steel or carbide bits are more rigid and in other ways superior to the toolholder-bit combination widely used on small lathes—but a conventional toolpost has too narrow a slot to accommodate them. Even if the slot were wide enough, some sort of block or shim system would have to be improvised to position cutting edges at the proper height.

Not so with the toolpost shown, however, since it was specifically designed to accommodate bits up to ½-in. wide. It has an easily set height-adjustment feature consisting of a steel ring supported by a quartet of bolts. It also provides firm support for boring bars or large bits ground as boring tools. All parts can be made of ordinary or tool steel, although for maximum durability, parts subjected to wear should be hardened.

Because of the wide tool slot, the diameter of the post is greater than that of the conventional

**EASY-TO-SHAPE PARTS** go together as shown in the exploded view below. Two setscrews may be needed.

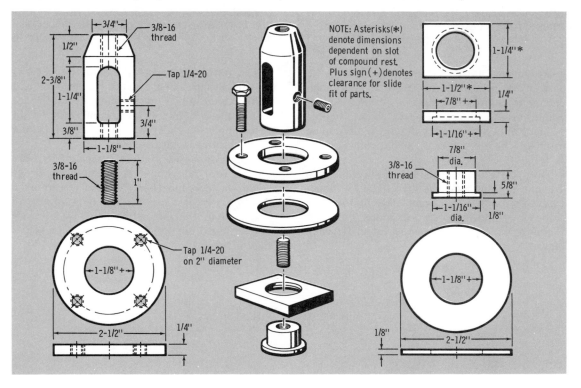

**TO CUT** a slot in the post, first drill two ½-in. holes about ¾ in. apart (measured center to center).

**MILLING** is the best way to remove the rest of the material. Alternately, excess could be sawn and filed.

**THE BUTTON** on the bottom of the post assembly is machined to fit T-slot, then fitted on ⅜-16-thread stud.

**THE BUTTON** should be a loose fit in the shouldered block. Check the clearance before removing the block.

post—yet the button and the block forming the base of the post assembly must be kept small enough to enter the toolpost T-slot on the compound rest. Therefore, the post assembly must be made in two sections so that the block can be installed (these sections are held together by the ⅜-16 stud).

The ¼-20 setscrew in the side of the holder will prevent possible side shifting of the bit, especially when it does not completely fill the wide slot. You could install two or more screws, if required, which would be most effective when the bit is making heavy side cuts.

The tool bit rests on a ring assembly consisting of a thick upper ring through which four ¼-20 bolts extend to rest on the thinner ring. By adjusting the 1-in.-long bolts to control the height of the upper ring, it's possible to set the bit at the proper cutting height.

The top bolt used to exert downward pressure on the tool bit should be a standard ⅜-16, square-head toolpost bolt. The dimensions in the drawing are for the holder shown, which will handle up to ½-in.-thick bits on a 9-in. lathe. Of course, for other lathes or different bit sizes, it may be necessary to vary dimensions.

# Lathe indexing attachment

■ THIS SIMPLE lathe indexing attachment is perfect for precision circular dividing and angular indexing. You can make it yourself.

The attachment consists of a U-shaped bracket which holds a single-thread worm, or tangent screw, graduated dial disc and an index that permits accurate settings. The unit is permanently mounted on the headstock of the lathe with a single bolt. One turn of the tangent screw turns the spindle 15° (since the spur gear on the spindle has 24 teeth).

The attachment is fitted with two dial discs:

One is divided into 60 parts, the second into 90. Between the two, you can graduate a circle to within ¼ to ⅙ of one degree. With appropriate setting of the dial, the circle can be divided into any even or odd number of parts.

The drawing (side view) shows the tangent screw engaged in the spindle spur gear. Directly below, the latter is shown when not in use. To engrave the lines, use a cutting tool mounted on the compound slide and determine the length by using the micrometer scale on the cross-feed screw.

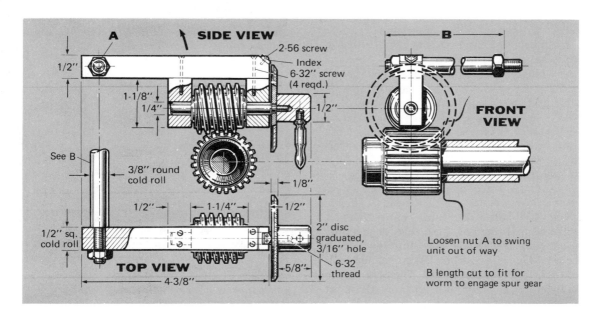

# Setscrew chucks you can make

■ A SIMPLE SETSCREW chuck for the headstock spindle of a lathe can be as useful as a costly three-jaw chuck. A setscrew chuck is commonly used for holding drill bits, end mills and Woodruff-keyway cutters. It can also hold workpieces, such as shafting, for turning or drilling. Setscrews bearing against the tool shank lock it in the chuck bore.

Setscrew chucks are often used in connection with a carriage-mounted milling attachment, with an angle plate or other arrangement for clamping and moving work in proper relation to drill bit, reamer, milling cutter, slitting saw, or other tool. Tools with shanks smaller than ½ in. can be mounted in the chucks with split bushings. The taper-shank type can be provided with two or more interchangeable heads having different hole diameters. A setscrew chuck can accommodate a conventional geared drill chuck with a ¼-in. shank projecting an inch or two.

There are two general types of setscrew chucks. As detailed here, chuck A screws over the spindle nose, and is preferable when minimum overhang is desirable and where the tool might be subjected to considerable side pressure. Chuck B has a taper shank fitting the spindle bore and a somewhat greater overhang.

Carefully made and fitted, either type can run as true as the average multijaw chuck or conventional drill chuck fitted with a taper shank.

• **Screw-on setscrew chuck.** This is screwed on the threaded end of the headstock spindle until firmly seated against the spindle shoulder. Cutting its thread is tricky. To fit a 9-in. lathe spindle, the thread is 1½-8 in a 1-in.-deep hole.

A 2-in. round steel blank about 2½ in. long is clamped in a three-jaw chuck, the end faced, and a ½-in. axial hole drilled 1 in. deep. With larger drills and a boring bar the hole is enlarged as required by the spindle-nose thread—here to about 1.345 in. dia., slightly larger than the standard 1.3376-in. for this thread. The bore diameter is further enlarged to a generous 1½ in. at both ends. Length of the inner, 1½-in.-diameter bore is determined by the clearance required by the threading tool—about ³⁄₁₆ in. To determine various dimensions of the threaded bore, the spindle nose and back plate of a chuck that fit the nose were used as guides.

The internal thread is cut next. Care must be

**MOUNTED** in screw-on setscrew (top photo), a Woodruff-keyway cutter is used to slot a ring. Work is held in carriage-mounted milling attachment. Taper-shank setscrew chuck (bottom photo) is better suited for drilling and operations in which pressure is lengthwise.

taken not to jam the end of the threading tool against the bore bottom. For each cut (average depth about 0.0025 in.), the lathe is stopped a bit short of the end, and the cut finished by pulling the headstock belt by hand. A 60° point threading bit is used.

Careful measurements can produce a precise fit of threads, but a gauge threaded like the spindle nose is handy for testing the internal threads. For another test remove the lathe chuck without loosening its jaws, turn it and the setscrew-chuck blank end for end, and try to screw the blank onto the spindle.

When the threading fits the spindle nose snugly, remove the workpiece from the chuck and drill a radial wrench hole (for a ¼-in. rod) as shown. This hole enables the chuck body to be loosened readily.

The chuck blank is installed on the spindle, and the outer end machined to the form shown. Then a hole is drilled through its center, starting with a small bit, to a diameter of about ⁷/₁₆ in. Because it is possible for a drill bit to produce a hole slightly out of line, a boring bar is used to bring the hole to final diameter of ½ in. This diameter depends on the tool-shank diameter and clearance necessary for easy installation or

removal of the tool, and might be around 0.501 or 0.502 in. (Many cutting tools have precise ½-in. shanks.) Another way to achieve an accurate, true-running hole is by internal grinding. If such a chuck is hardened, final grinding would be done afterward.

After the outside surface has been smoothed with file and abrasive cloth, remove the chuck body from the spindle and drill and tap the two ¼-20 setscrew holes. Make an internal back-up disc (part Y) to help the setscrews handle end thrust such as that which is produced when a large-diameter drill is driven by the chuck.

The steel disc covers the hole and has an outside diameter that fits inside the headstock-spindle hole without jamming. Two 6-32 bolts with heads filed for clearance anchor it in place. (Four would be stronger.) Disc can be removed when chucking long shanks or rods.

• **Taper-shank setscrew chuck.** This is sometimes used on drill-press spindles. The shank shown is from a broken No. 2 Morse taper twist drill. The drill is annealed and the flute section sawed off. Then the shank is installed in the lathe spindle, and punch-marked for later alignment with spindle sleeve and spindle itself.

The projecting portion is machined to ½-in.

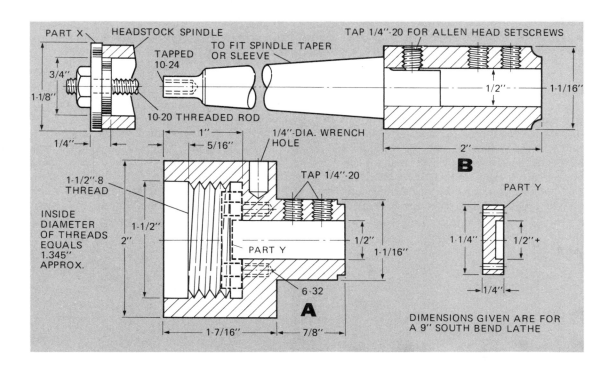

**FLOOD THE WORK** with a sulfurized cutting oil when you bore the spindle-nose recess in the chuck body.

**AFTER RECESS** is bored, 1½-in. x 8 threads are cut into the chuck body to fit the 9-in. lathe spindle.

**REGULAR TWIST DRILL** is used to bore a slightly undersized axial hole in the body of the screw-on chuck.

**BORING BAR** is used to finish-bore the axial hole. The hole in the side is for a chuck-removing wrench.

diameter and a setscrew-flat filed on it.

The chuck body is made from 1⅛-in. steel rod. It is chucked, and an axial hole about $7/16$ in. in diameter bored through. The outer ¾ in. of this hole is bored so that the taper-shank end, previously machined to ½ in., will fit snugly. Then the piece is unchucked, and a hole for the setscrew that clamps it to the shank is drilled and taped for a ¼-20 thread. The two parts are assembled and

installed in the lathe spindle for final boring of the ½-in. tool-shank hole, and finishing the surface.

Because the taper shank might come loose when in use, a safety feature is added—a long, threaded rod extending from the tapered shank through a cap machined to fit the outer end of the headstock spindle. A nut tightened against this cap, part X, locks the shank in place.

# Swing toolholder for your lathe

■ ONE OF THE MOST bothersome tasks in lathe work is adjusting the tool bit to the correct height. With this universal swing-away-type toolholder, you can check the progress of thread cutting simply by swinging the tool upward.

The holder is made to fit a 7-in. lathe and the jaw is milled to accept ⅜-in.-square-shank bits. To make frictional adjustments so the holder swings without play or binding, you simply tighten the ¼-in. capscrews in the pivot pin. Use a single bolt to attach the holder to the cross slide.

**PIVOTED** to block bolted to cross slide, cutting tool is swung upward and clear to check progress.

**FOR ORDINARY** turning or thread cutting, holder is swung around so toolholding jaw is at right angle.

**FOR INTERNAL** boring or thread cutting, toolholding jaw is positioned so it is parallel to lathe.

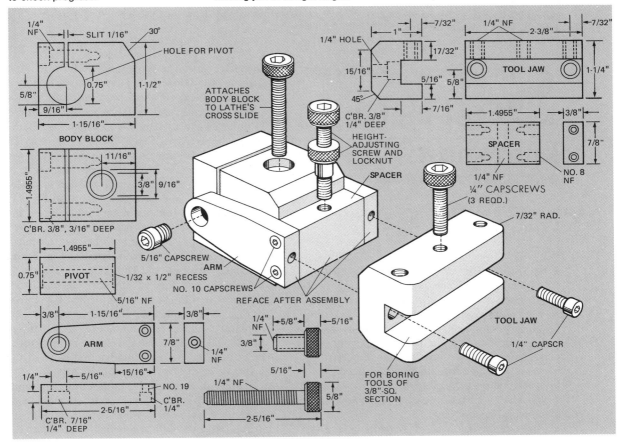

WEAR SAFETY GOGGLES

**CUTTING SHEET-METAL** stock calls for a saber saw or portable jigsaw as shown above; snips, several of which are shown in Fig. 25; or professional equipment such as the squaring shear shown in Fig. 2. Ordinary snips take care of metal as thick as 22 ga. handily. To follow a pattern accurately, it's important to score lines clearly on the surface of the metal, then to follow those lines carefully. When possible, use a straightedge to keep the scribe on the track.

# Sheet-metal know-how

■ BASIC SHEET-METAL WORK requires only metal snips or shears and a squared hardwood block or two over which to make bends. Anvils, more tools and shaping devices, and bench stakes for seams and radius bends will let you go beyond simple projects. Beyond this point, you enter the professional area with its hand and powered machines and advanced ways to develop sheet-metal shapes.

Whatever your level may be, you'll find sheet-metal work is satisfying.

Three basic methods of developing a given shape are shown in representative form in Figs. 3 through 6. These by no means cover the field of development, but do indicate methods of procedure. The shortcut, rollation method in Fig. 3 is quite widely used in the development of the more simple forms. Figs. 12 and 14 through 16 show how it is carried out when making the top of a funnel or similar bell shape. The joint in the funnel top, or bell, can be seamed as in detail A, Fig. 11, and hammered flat as in Fig. 12, or can be sweat-soldered before soldering on the neck, Fig. 11, B. For procedure in laying down a conical shape (or what is to become a conical shape) note the right-hand detail in Fig. 3 and compare with Fig. 14. The cutout in Fig. 14 is then bent as in Fig. 15 and the edges chalked. The final step in the rollation method is pictured in Fig. 16. The other development methods such as parallel-line development, Fig. 4, radial-line development, Fig. 5 and development by triangulation, Fig. 6, are used in advanced work in the laying down of large and involved shapes.

Nearly all sheet metals, both ferrous and nonferrous, of 22 ga. or thinner can be cut easily with ordinary tinner's snips, Figs. 14 and 25. Heavier metal is best cut with compound-lever shears, or

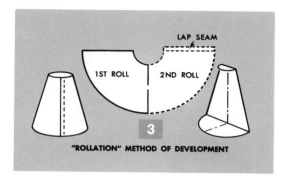

**FOOT-OPERATED** squaring shears like this are standard in professional or large school shops.

with a hacksaw with a blade having at least 24 teeth per inch. You also can use a portable jigsaw (or saber saw), Fig. 1, with a metal-cutting blade. Many sheet-metal shops and some school shops have a squaring shear, Fig. 2. Foot-operated units of this latter type usually handle mild steel to 16 ga. with a nominal cutting width of 30 in. or more.

Hand-wiring an edge, Fig. 8, is a good test of one's skill as a tinsmith. In shops this job usually is done on a machine, Fig. 17, but you can do a creditable job by hand as in Fig. 8, using a wood mallet and a pair of pliers, as in the accompanying photo, Fig. 7. Start with a right-angle bend in the sheet as in detail A. Turn it back on itself with the wire inside as in detail B, using the mallet and the pliers in conjunction to make a smooth bend. Wiring usually is done before the part is formed. You'll find wired edges on such commonplace items as pails, pans, funnels, garden carts—almost any open-top container made from sheet metal. A wired edge adds greatly to their strength, durability and appearance.

Another step in simple forming that you should be familiar with before tackling any type of corner joining is the method of notching and clipping at corners to produce neat, attractive work. The square notch, used on simple boxlike forms, permits corners to be fitted tightly, details C and D, Fig. 9. The V-notch can be cut as in detail B, producing an overlap for riveting or soldering, or can be cut as in detail A to form a neat corner without an overlap. It also is used for double seaming on work having inside flanges. Bend the flanges against a solid hardwood block as in detail E, using a wood mallet or a soft hammer to prevent denting or scoring the metal.

Progressive steps in making a dovetail seam of one type are shown in Fig. 13. This method is

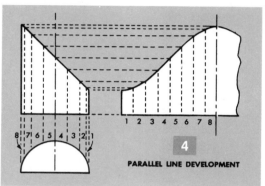

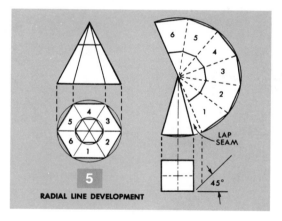

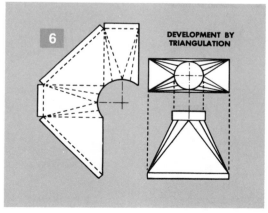

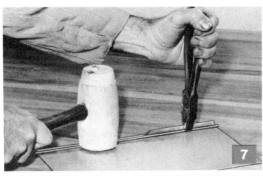

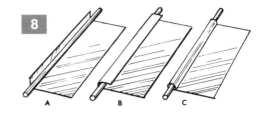

**WIRING AN EDGE** by hand tests tinsmith's skill. Photo at the left shows how mallet and pliers are used together to bend the edge. The detail drawings above show the three basic steps in the hand-wiring process.

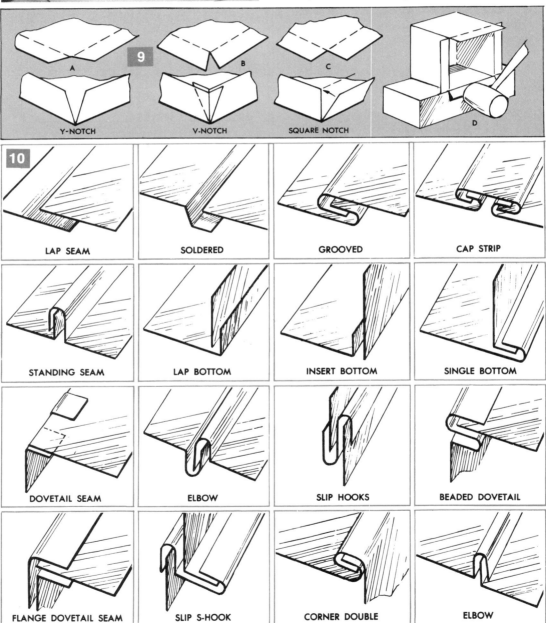

Y-NOTCH    V-NOTCH    SQUARE NOTCH

| LAP SEAM | SOLDERED | GROOVED | CAP STRIP |
| STANDING SEAM | LAP BOTTOM | INSERT BOTTOM | SINGLE BOTTOM |
| DOVETAIL SEAM | ELBOW | SLIP HOOKS | BEADED DOVETAIL |
| FLANGE DOVETAIL SEAM | SLIP S-HOOK | CORNER DOUBLE | ELBOW |

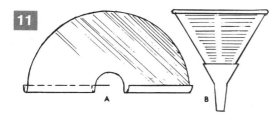

IN CUTTING a funnel top or bell, leave room for a lap joint at an end—or a grooved joint at both ends. Use of the rollation pattern is shown in Figs. 14 through 16.

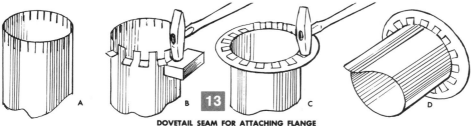

DOVETAIL SEAM FOR ATTACHING FLANGE

often used when joining a flange to a cylindrical shape. The latter is scribed near the end with a visible line and is then clipped at spaced intervals as in detail A, the cuts stopping at the scribed line. Next the alternate tabs are bent out and at right angles as in detail B. Now the flange is cut and slipped over the remaining vertical tabs, which are finally bent outward over the flange as in detail C. The finished job is shown in detail D. For added strength the tabs may be sweat-soldered.

Fig. 10 details various types of locking seams and typical soldered seams that are commonly used in joining sheet metals. Most of these can be formed on a bar folder, Fig. 21. Of course, the seams are not shown as they will appear when completed. They are shown open, or unlocked, to indicate the relationship of the folded edges. Some of the seams must be sweat-soldered, of course. While most of these bends are made by machine, some can be made easily by hand with the simplest tools. You will find these seams on various types of metal containers, in sheet-metal duct work, furnace plenums—anywhere sheet-metal parts are to be corner-joined or in some cases joined end to end.

Figs. 17, 18 and 20 picture a hand-powered unit known in tinshops as a rotary machine. It is supplied with interchangeable rolls and can be set up quickly to do crimping, beading, wiring, burring, and a number of other related operations. The machines generally are of two types,

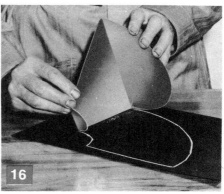

**A STANDARD** rotary machine is regular equipment in most sheet-metal shops. Here an edge is wired.

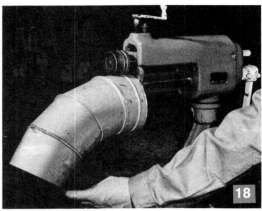

**THIS ROTARY** machine has a deep throat. Here a bead is being rolled on a smoke-pipe elbow.

the standard unit, Fig. 17 and the deep-throated unit, Figs. 18 and 20. A wiring operation is pictured in Fig. 17 and beading and crimping operations in Figs. 18 and 20.

In the well-equipped commercial shops and also in school shops you'll probably find an assortment of stakes and a bench plate. Fig. 19 illustrates only a few of the many types of stakes available for various types of sheet-metal work at the bench. One that is quite common,is the double stake, supplied with at least four heads, A, B, C, and D. Light sheet metals are worked on stakes and hollow mandrels.

Fig. 22 shows how the single hemmed edge is formed on a bar-type folding machine, Fig. 21. Fig. 23, details A, B and C, show the forming of a double-hemmed edge. In one method of making a grooved seam by hand, the locks on the two pieces of metal are folded and hooked together and the seam closed with a hand groov-

ing tool, Fig. 24. The seam is then flattened with a wood mallet. The seaming tool, Fig. 25, enables one to do a better job of working a seam. It comes in widths up to 6 in. or more and facilitates making a sharp, clean bend. It is adjustable for depth, or reach, which determines the distance from the edge the bend is made.

Cylindrical forms can be made by working the metal over a hollow mandrel with a mallet, Fig. 19, or with a slip-roll former, Fig. 26. Straight cuts in the light sheet metals of 22 ga. and thinner are easily made with tin snips of the regular pattern, Fig. 25. For making short-radius circular cuts in from an edge you'll need the hawk's-bill snips. For intricate patterns involving curved cuts of medium radius you use what are known as pocket circular snips (not illustrated). Aviation snips, Fig. 25, come right and left and in combination and are designed for intricate work on light sheet metals.

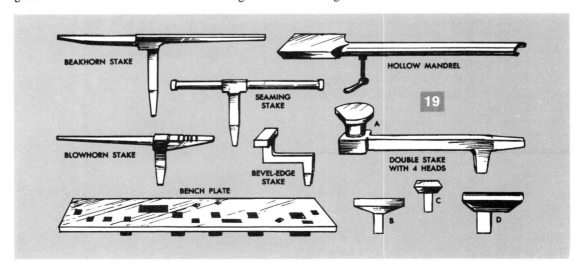

BEAKHORN STAKE

HOLLOW MANDREL

SEAMING STAKE

19

BLOWHORN STAKE

BEVEL-EDGE STAKE

DOUBLE STAKE WITH 4 HEADS

BENCH PLATE

A

B

C

D

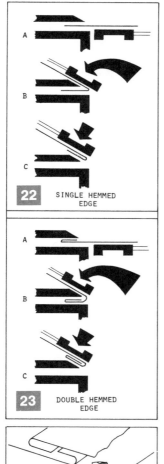

**22** SINGLE HEMMED EDGE

**23** DOUBLE HEMMED EDGE

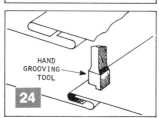

HAND GROOVING TOOL

**24**

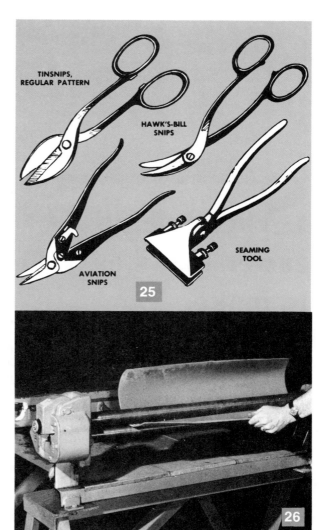

TINSNIPS, REGULAR PATTERN

HAWK'S-BILL SNIPS

AVIATION SNIPS

SEAMING TOOL

**25**

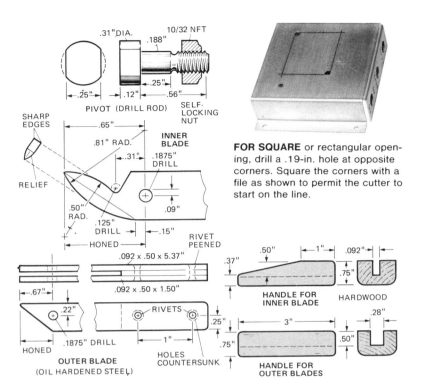

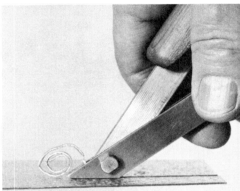

**FOR SQUARE** or rectangular opening, drill a .19-in. hole at opposite corners. Square the corners with a file as shown to permit the cutter to start on the line.

**CENTER BLADE** of cutter removes a narrow strip of metal in the form of a curl.

# Sheet-metal cutter that's easy to make

■ THIS EASY-TO-MAKE sheet-metal cutter will do things you can't do with regular snips. It will cut in the center of a sheet with a .19-in.-dia. starting hole and cut on either the upper or lower side of the sheet, whichever is more convenient. It works best on straight cuts but it will cut a large radius.

As the blades cut, they curl a strip of metal ahead of the cutter. There is practically no distortion of the metal from the cutting action. The cutter will handle up to .06-in. aluminum or .02-in. soft-steel sheet.

The blades are made of oil-hardening tool steel. This steel is sold at machine-shop supply houses in strips two feet long. One strip is enough for one cutter. Finish the blades completely before heat treating as the steel will not distort during heating. To harden the blades, heat to a bright red (1475° F. to 1525° F.) and quench in motor oil. Draw the blades in a kitchen oven at 350° F. for an hour. Following the heat treatment, polish the blades and hone the cutting edges.

The hardwood handles are fastened to the blades with epoxy cement. Use a self-locking nut on the pivot bolt and adjust it so the blades work freely.

# Sheet-metal brake you make of wood

**THE SHEET-METAL BRAKE,** made of standard-size lumber, handles up to 26-gauge metal.

**LONG PIECES OF METAL** are as easy to bend as smaller ones with this homemade brake. You simply change the pressure foot.

■ NEAT right-angle bends and flat folds are easy to make with this simple, benchtop, sheet-metal brake. The metal is inserted under the pressure plate, the two handles are tightened and the hinged forming bar across the front is brought up to make the desired degree of bend. To flatfold an edge, you first bring the forming bar all the way up and against the beveled pressure plate; then the work is removed, flipped over and the bend is squeezed flat.

The brake is made mostly of wood of standard lumberyard sizes. Nuts, which are sweat-soldered in place, provide the tapped holes for each threaded handle, and the yokes are bent from strap iron to straddle the two hinged pressure arms. A compression spring under each arm raises the arms automatically when its handle is backed off.

To bend a metal box, the trick is to bend two opposite sides using the regular pressure plate.

Then a special pressure plate is cut to fit the inside width of the box and only one pressure arm is used to hold the plate while making the bend. You can fashion boxes as small as 3x4 in.

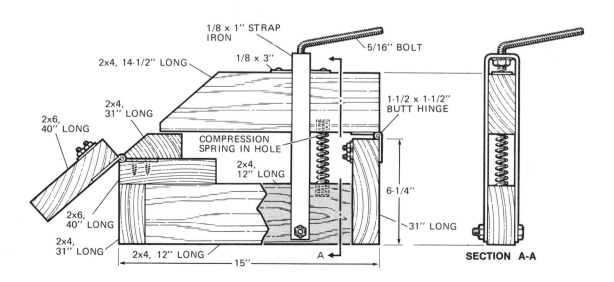

1/8 x 1" STRAP IRON

5/16" BOLT

2x4, 14-1/2" LONG

1/8 x 3"

2x4, 31" LONG

2x6, 40" LONG

1-1/2 x 1-1/2" BUTT HINGE

COMPRESSION SPRING IN HOLE

2x4, 12" LONG

2x6, 40" LONG

6-1/4"

2x4, 31" LONG

2x4, 12" LONG

31" LONG

15"

A

SECTION A-A

# Shop forge you can build

■ THIS FORGE IS MADE with a cast-off barbecue grill, legs from an old kitchen stool, some firebrick and a sheet-metal hood. The blower can be purchased at an electronics supply house. You'll need a length of flexible exhaust pipe to fit the inside diameter of the blower outlet. The squirrel-cage blower is mounted on a metal flange attached to one leg. Wires from the blower pass through an outlet box containing a dimmer switch.

The grill is mounted on the stool legs with ¼-in. bolts. Secure the flexible pipe to the bottom of the barbecue grill by attaching a 90° pipe elbow to the grill with a U-bolt. Then add a nipple to the elbow to accept the flexible pipe. Fill the grill with sand level with the opening of the pipe elbow, then set four firebricks on edge around the hole.

Make the hood from sheet metal, a length of vent pipe and an elbow. Use Pop rivets to fasten the hood sections together.

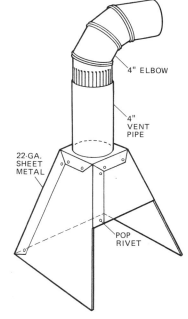

4" ELBOW

4" VENT PIPE

22-GA. SHEET METAL

POP RIVET

**FASTEN** 90° elbow to bottom of grill with U-bolt.

**ADD SAND,** level with elbow, then set four firebrick on edge around hole.

**MOUND FIREPIT** with handfuls of briquets; light with fluid and match.

**USE LIGHT-DIMMER** switch to control blower speed, regulating air to firepit.

**KEEP BLOWER** at low speed until most coals glow bright red.

# Superhot furnace for metalworking

■ THE GREATEST OBSTACLE for someone who wants to get started in metal sculpture or jewelry-making is usually the high cost of equipment for melting metal. An oxyacetylene torch with the necessary tips, tanks, gauges and pressure regulators is a sizable investment. But you can make a crucible furnace like this one for a fraction of the cost.

It can provide temperatures ranging from about 900° F. to over 2700° F. That's hot enough to let you work with pewter, zinc, aluminum, bronze, brass, copper, precious metals and even iron and steel.

The combustion chamber is made of high-duty (about 3600° F.) insulating firebrick and, for mortar, an air-setting, high-alumina-content, refractory cement. It is assembled from eight bricks—two used as is, six cut to the shape shown. The cutting is done easily with a jigsaw, bandsaw or sabre saw. Begin assembly by soaking all the bricks in clean water until thoroughly sodden. Premix the mortar with clean water, in a clean container, until it has a smooth and creamy consistency like that of cake batter.

Hand-dip the two uncut bricks in mortar and place them side by side to form a flat 2½ x 9 x 9-in. base. Use a small paintbrush dipped in mortar to smooth out any lumps and fill any holes. Add the other layers, two mortar-dipped bricks at a time, alternating the direction of the joints and using the paintbrush and mortar to smooth and fill.

Bake the combustion chamber at 400° to 500° F. in the kitchen oven until it is completely dry. The tuyere hole is cut through the second-layer wall on a tangent to the inner surface. A scrap of 1-in. pipe, turned by hand, will quickly and

**WHEN THE CRUCIBLE** is glowing brightly, use tongs to put in an ingot of metal.

**STIR THE MOLTEN** metal with a green stick to bring the dross (oxides and dirt) to the surface.

**USE LARGE TONGS** to remove the crucible full of molten metal from the furnace. Use safety equipment.

**POUR METAL** from the heated crucible into your mold using shorter tongs.

neatly make this opening. Finally, add a galvanized sheet-iron case to protect the brittle firebrick.

### Making the burner

The burner consists of an air-gas mixing chamber and nozzle (tuyere) and forced-air blower with speed control. Make the orifice pipe from a 3-in. long nipple of ⅛-in. black pipe. Drill a ³⁄₃₂-in. hole through one wall at the midpoint.

The tuyere is made from an 8 or 9-in. length of 1-in. black pipe, with holes to accommodate the orifice pipe drilled through both walls 6 or 7 in. from one end. Braze the orifice pipe in place with the orifice facing inward. Cap one end and install a gas cock on the other. The blower is taken from any hair dryer, and a solid-state light dimmer is added for a speed control.

### Installation and use

Any site that is suitable for welding will serve, assuming that it has good ventilation and that natural gas and well-grounded electrical service are available.

Set up the combustion chamber on the floor and insert the tuyere into the combustion chamber—to, but not past, the inner wall. Connect the blower and speed control. Ground the tuyere and combustion-chamber case. Connect the natural-gas line.

Prepare for operation by assembling molds, crucibles, tongs, asbestos gloves, safety goggles and the metal to be cast. Place the crucible in the center of the combustion chamber; this aids heat circulation and makes the crucible easier to re-

move. Start the blower, then open the gas cock a little and ignite the burner immediately from the top of the combustion chamber. Over a 30-minute period, increase the gas flow to maximum, continually adjusting the blower speed for a pale blue flame.

When the furnace has reached its maximum temperature, the inner wall will glow a brilliant yellow. Once the crucible is glowing hot, you can put metal into it.

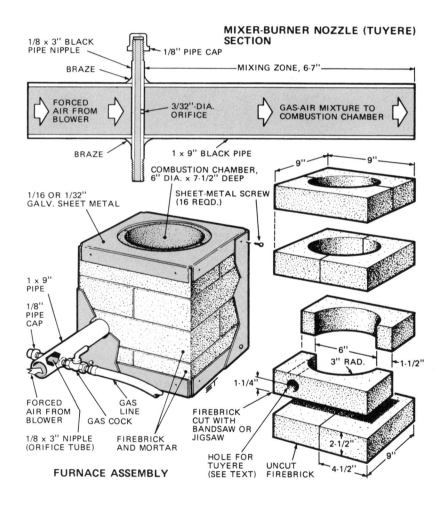

MIXER-BURNER NOZZLE (TUYERE) SECTION

FURNACE ASSEMBLY

**POWDERED MOLD** material is poured into a small dish and then mixed with water to a creamy paste. Stir it gently to avoid whipping up air bubbles in the mix.

**A METAL TUBE,** called a ring or flask, serves as a container for the soupy mold mix. Fill it flush to the top. You can use a flexible dish to make pouring easy.

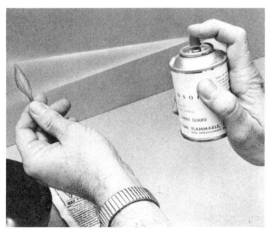

**SPRAY THE PATTERN**—in this case a small leaf—with a wetting agent before embedding it. This lets the mold mix flow smoothly over the entire surface.

# Metal castings you can make yourself

■ THERE'S A BIG thrill in seeing a design you have created yourself turn almost magically into gleaming metal. But maybe you figure this requires special know-how and a lot of fancy equipment.

Not today. Hobby shops stock everything you need to cast small model parts or pieces of jewelry in glittering gold, silver and other metals. The process, known as investment or "lost wax" casting, is the same as that used centuries ago by early Egyptians. You carve the shape you want in soft wax, embed the wax in a plaster-like material that hardens around it, then bake it in an oven. Under high heat, the wax vaporizes—is literally "lost"—leaving an empty mold. Molten metal forced into the mold then produces an exact copy of the original wax pattern.

You can make your own wax patterns using a special carving wax, or you can buy patterns ready to use. The latter come in a wide variety of ornaments, charms and small pieces of jewelry. You can also copy actual specimens, such as leaves and insects—anything that will vaporize at 1200° F., leaving little ash.

The equipment you'll need includes a small electric oven for burning out the wax, a propane hand torch for melting the metal, an air pump for

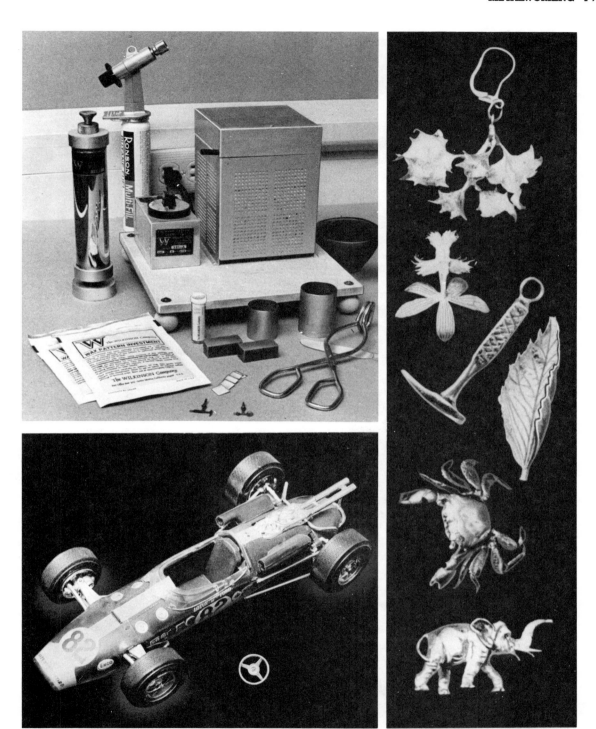

**EQUIPMENT YOU NEED** for metal casting is shown at upper left. Main items are (l. to r.) a hand air pump, propane torch and electric burnout oven. Other supplies are powdered mold mix (in packets), metal tubes to hold the mold, blocks of carving wax, tongs, small metal ingots, wax sprues and a mixing dish, preferably a flexible rubber or plastic. Tiny steering wheel for the model racing car at lower left and charms and trinkets at right are examples of the many intricate shapes you can cast by lost-wax method.

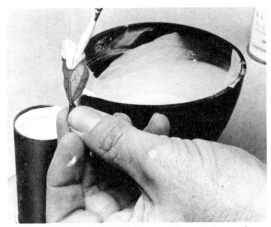

**ON INTRICATE OBJECTS,** it's best to coat the surface with the mold mix first, using a brush. This insures that the mix will get into all the crevices.

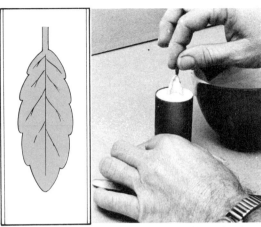

**THE PRECOATED** pattern is now dipped into the ring containing mold mix. Be sure it is submerged and fully surrounded by the mix with no air pockets.

**PLACE THE MOLD** in the oven crater-side down. Burnout takes from 30 to 60 minutes for wax patterns. Less combustible materials may need several hours.

**FILL THE MOLD'S** crater with several small metal ingots after the burnout. Play the torch flame over them until a ball of molten metal is formed.

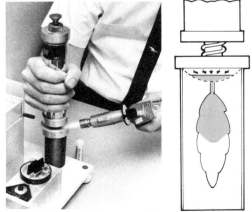

**PRESS THE PUMP** down over the mold ring without removing the torch. The pump's pressure forces the molten metal down in the mold, as the sketch shows.

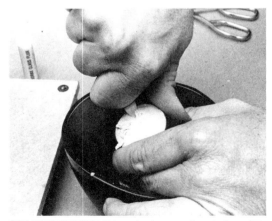

**SOAKING THE MOLD** in water loosens it and allows it to be peeled away from the casting. The remaining bits can easily be taken off with a toothbrush.

**LET THE MOLD** harden for 45 minutes or so, then scoop out a shallow crater on top to hold the metal. Be sure that this exposes the sprue on the pattern.

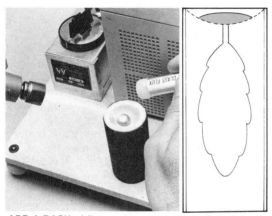

**ADD A DASH** of flux to the molten metal. This reduces oxides that produce a crust. The sketch shows how the metal forms a puddle above the empty mold.

**FINISHED CASTING** can be polished to a sparkle with a small buffing wheel like the one shown. Use tripoli or jeweler's rouge for best results.

forcing the molten metal into the mold, and a supply of metal tubes, called rings or flasks, in which the molds are formed. The rings come in a variety of diameters depending on the size of the pattern you want to copy. The mold material, called the "investment," is a white powder that's mixed with water to form a creamy paste.

It's important to use clean metal as dirt particles can result in an imperfectly formed casting. It's also important not to trap air bubbles around the wax pattern when embedding it in the mold. Tiny bubbles leave pockmarks in the mold.

The accompanying photos show the procedure for making a typical casting. Before the pattern is embedded in the investment material, it's necessary to add a small stem, called a "sprue," so it sticks up through the mold to the top. When the sprue, usually made of wax, melts away, it leaves a tiny hole in the mold. This enables you to get molten metal down into the mold cavity from the outside.

### Casting the metal

Note that the molten metal will not just flow down the sprue hole by itself—surface tension prevents it. You must actually force the metal into the mold under pressure, and this is what's known as "casting." The usual casting device is a small hand-operated air pump. Pressure is first built up in the pump by giving the plunger about 15 strokes. Then the pump is placed over the investment ring and pressed down. This releases the air, driving the molten metal into the mold.

Hold the pump over the mold 30 seconds until the metal has become completely solidified or "frozen." To remove your casting from the mold, place the mold in a bowl of water. Allow it to stay there until the water has completely soaked into the material. This should cause the mold to break away easily from the casting. Breaking renders the mold unusable a second time.

It's quite likely that the casting will appear discolored. This discoloration is a surface oxide and is easily removed by pickling the casting in an acid solution—two parts muriatic acid to one part water is usual.

After pickling, remove the sprue stem from the casting with a pair of wire-cutting pliers. Then grind or file off the remaining stub. The best method of polishing your casting is with some type of rotating polisher. The most common compounds used for final finishing are tripoli and jeweler's rouge, applied with a soft buffing wheel.

# Model this 24-pounder

■ IF YOU ARE a dyed-in-the-wool model-maker, you know that plastic models can't begin to give you the satisfaction and pride of accomplishment you get from building an authentic replica from scratch. You'll get such a charge from modeling and displaying this 24-pounder from the main battery of the U.S. frigate *Constitution*.

While both English and American types of 24-pounders were in *Old Ironside's* complement of guns, this model, in gleaming brass and contrasting walnut, is patterned after the 12 American-type guns which were deployed at the forward and after ports. It's based on original shipyard plans which were followed in the 1927-1931 restoration of the *Constitution*.

The original guns measured 9 ft., 5¾ in. in length and were of gray cast iron. The wooden carriages were of white oak, and most of the fittings were steel. The barrel of our model is brass and is approximately 5½ in. long, which makes it about 1/20th actual size.

Carriages for the guns in the main battery varied in size according to the gun deck, and the heights of the carriage bed blocks, which were used for elevating the barrel, were determined by trial during firing missions.

All the metal parts of the model are brass; the wooden parts are walnut. Clear lacquer is used to keep the polished brass from tarnishing; the walnut carriage is finished natural.

Most of the dimensions are given in decimals. This is particularly true in the case of the gun barrel since the tool feed of a lathe on which it is turned is measured in thousandths of an inch. If you prefer to work in fractions, you can convert the measurements with the aid of a decimal-equivalent table.

The gun-barrel blank is a 1-in. brass rod about 7 in. long. This length was selected as a convenient size for the lathe used in making the complete pilot model. Because a 3-jaw chuck would cut down on the usable length, the rod was center-drilled and mounted between centers, and driven by a dog made from the outer ring of a ball bearing having a 1-in. bore. However, any similar ring will do. If your lathe lacks bed length to drill the center holes with a bit in a tailstock chuck, lay out centers carefully and use a center drill in a drill press.

When machining the barrel, follow the drawings on these pages. To form the rounded bands and contours, machine them with square edges, then round them with a fine file or a hand-held chisel.

Trunnions are usually an integral part of a real cannon. In the model barrel, however, they are cut from brass rod. To drill the hole in the barrel for this rod, use the jig detailed in the drawing. If you lack an L-size drill (.290-in. dia.) you can make a 9/32 or 19/64-in. hole and match the trunnion notches in the carriage. The rod forming the trunnions can be a drive fit or held with a setscrew on the underside of the barrel.

To bore out the barrel, use a $^9/_{32}$-in. twist drill, starting at the center hole in the muzzle end. The drawing shows the bore full length, as in the original cannon, but in the model it need extend only to the trunnion hole, enough to keep the barrel from being muzzle-heavy.

The powder-igniting arrangement on top of the breech is formed as shown. The teardrop recess is a separate piece of brass soldered or cemented with epoxy to the barrel. V-shaped sighting notches on top and each side of the barrel can be hand-filed or scribed while the barrel is in the lathe. To do this, move the lathe carriage back and forth and feed a pointed tool so it shaves a notch .018-in. wide.

Before removing the barrel, polish it with very fine abrasive cloth. Then use a brass polish for a final luster. After cutting scrap from the breech carefully smooth and polish the rounded end. If you solder the powder "pan" to the barrel, re-polish the metal to remove heat discoloration.

Full-size patterns for wooden parts on the gun carriage are shown in the diagram. As for the sides, made in pairs, you'll find it helpful to make a master pattern from aluminum or cardboard, then drill the ring and tie-bolt holes in it. Saw both sides at one time, tape the template to them, then drill the holes slightly smaller than the eye-bolts. Note that the sides taper upward slightly from the base to top.

Carriage parts are shaped from black walnut and glued in the order shown. The trucks of the original cannon were built up in layers, as detailed for the model, but you can cut them from ¼-in. stock and represent the joints with knife cuts. Note that hind trucks are smaller than the fore trucks. Use tiny brass escutcheon pins for rivets.

**HOMEMADE "PLUG CUTTER"** from ⅛-in. pipe is used in drill press to round ends of wooden axle-tree parts.

**THIN MILLING CUTTER**, on head spindle arbor, cuts the walnut side members of the gun carriage.

**CUTS AT RIGHT ANGLE** to the first ones are made in both side pieces at the same time; finish by hand.

**CARRIAGE TRUCKS** are turned to their final diameter by mounting discs on arbor of 5/16-in. bolt and two nuts.

**BARREL BLANK**, mounted between centers, is driven by faceplate dog made from a ball-bearing ring.

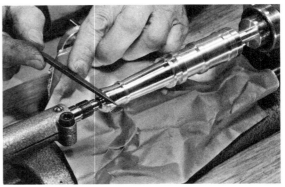

**AFTER RIDGES** are machined square, they're rounded with Swiss-type file as done here at end of muzzle.

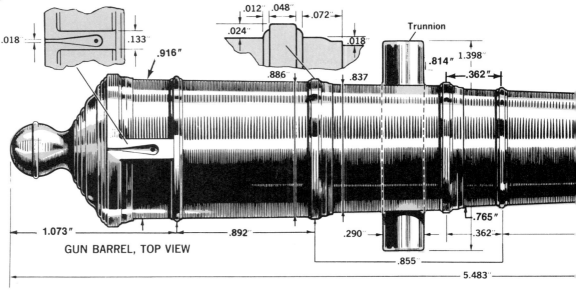

GUN BARREL, TOP VIEW

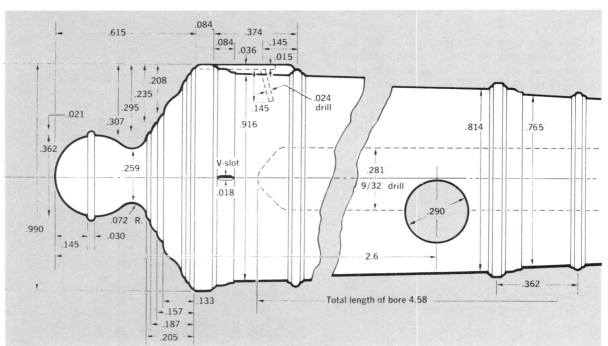

**HAND-HELD CHISEL** resting on blank bit clamped in toolholder is used to shape final breech contours.

**COMPLETED BARREL** is polished in the lathe with a brass polish; ball end is hand-finished later.

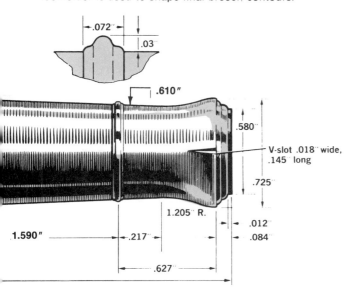

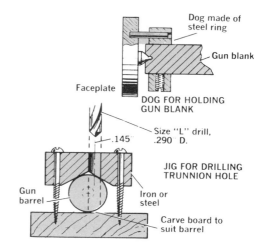

**JIG IS USED** to drill hole through barrel for trunnion rod. Masking tape protects the barrel.

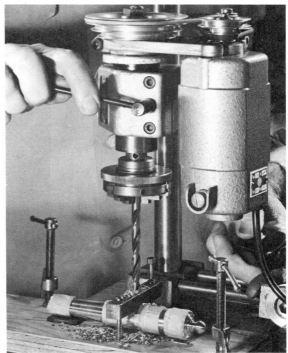

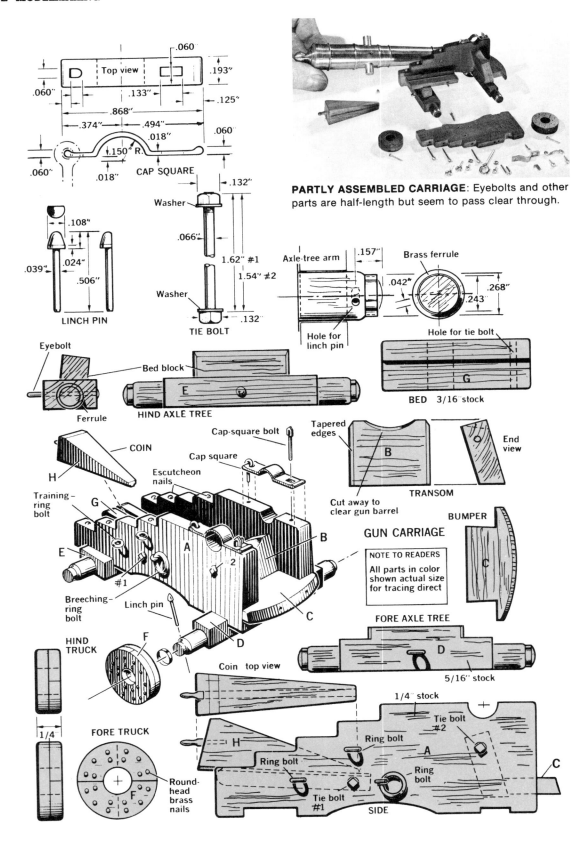

.060

D Top view .193″

.060″ .133″ .125″

.868″

.374″ .494″ .060

.018″ .150″ R.

.060″ .018″ CAP SQUARE

**PARTLY ASSEMBLED CARRIAGE:** Eyebolts and other parts are half-length but seem to pass clear through.

.108″

.039″ .024″ .506″

LINCH PIN

Washer .132″

.066″

1.62″ #1

1.54″ #2

Washer

.132″

TIE BOLT

Axle-tree arm .157″ Brass ferrule

.042″ .268″ .243

Hole for linch pin Hole for tie bolt

Eyebolt Bed block

E G

Ferrule HIND AXLE TREE BED 3/16″ stock

Cap-square bolt Tapered edges

COIN Cap square B End view

H Escutcheon nails

Training-ring bolt G Cut away to clear gun barrel TRANSOM

E A BUMPER

B

#1 2 GUN CARRIAGE C

Breeching-ring bolt Linch pin NOTE TO READERS All parts in color shown actual size for tracing direct FORE AXLE TREE

C

HIND TRUCK D D

F 5/16″ stock

1/4

FORE TRUCK Coin top view 1/4″ stock

Tie bolt #2

1/4 H Ring bolt

Round-head brass nails A

F Ring bolt Ring bolt

Tie bolt #1 SIDE C

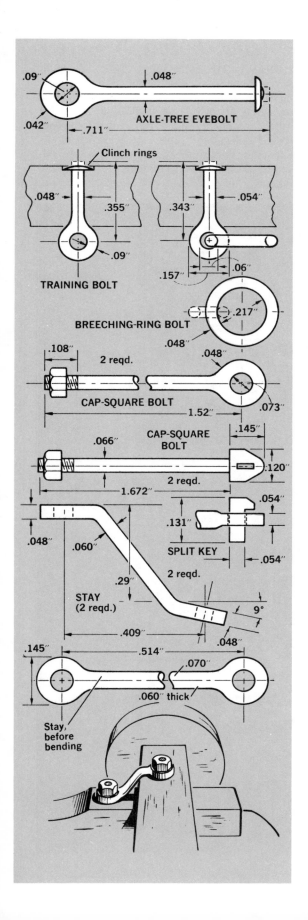

.09"
.048"
.042"
.711"
**AXLE-TREE EYEBOLT**

Clinch rings

.048"
.355"
.343"
.054"
.09"
**TRAINING BOLT**
.157"
.06"

.217"
**BREECHING-RING BOLT**
.048"

.108"
2 reqd.
.048"
**CAP-SQUARE BOLT**
1.52"
.073"

.145"
.066"
**CAP-SQUARE BOLT**
2 reqd.
1.672"
.120"

.054"
.048"
.060"
.131"
**SPLIT KEY**
.054"
.29"
**STAY (2 reqd.)**
2 reqd.
9°
.409"
.048"

.145"
.514"
.070"
.060" thick
**Stay, before bending**

Round ends of the fore and hind axle trees can be "turned" to fit the trucks with a homemade plug cutter chucked in the drill press. It's made from ⅛-in. pipe reamed with a ⁵/₁₆-in. twist drill. Form teeth around one end with a file. Axletree ferrules are turned from brass rod and bored to form a press-fit ring.

Tie bolts and cap-square bolts are shown full length, but you can simulate them merely by inserting the "heads" of the bolts in shallow undersize holes. Likewise, the eyes of the eyebolts need not be solid rings, as shown. Simply form an eye with needle-nose pliers and force it into the wood so you can't see the open end. If you can find actual bolts and nuts from junked timepieces, your model will look more authentic.

Cut stays for the fore axle tree from .060-in. brass sheet, then file, drill and bend to shape. Shape the linch pins from fair-size brass escutcheon pins, filing a flat on their heads to clear the axle trucks.

Cap squares that clamp over the trunnions can be shaped from .060-in. brass. File away the middle portion to .024-in. thick, then cut the piece in half lengthwise to form the two cap squares. Round the thick ends remaining as shown and form the slots by drilling and filing. Brass should be soft enough to bend easily around the trunnions. Note that one end of the cap squares pivots on an eyebolt while the slot in the opposite end engages a bolt with a slotted "head." A brass split key fits the slot and locks the cap square around the trunnion.

The base represents a section of sloping deck and ship rail. Make it of walnut to match the carriage or of lighter, contrasting wood. For a darker tone than you get with clear lacquer, rub in boiled linseed oil and let dry a day or two. Or seal the first or second application with thinned shellac (after oil has dried), sand lightly and apply a final lacquer coat.

# $\mathbf{M}$odeling fine ships—a challenge

■ RECREATING IN MINIATURE the majesty of an ancient sailing ship is a rewarding challenge, filled with fun and excitement, that any hobbyist can master. Making an authentic replica of a mighty square rigger used to be considered beyond the skills of the average do-it-yourselfer, requiring expert know-how, specialized tools and massive amounts of time and patience. Time and patience are still requisites,

but beyond these the task is not necessarily as awesome as it might seem. Authentic construction plans are available from a variety of sources. Books, tools, materials and even ready-made parts can be obtained at hobby shops. Power tools make the job easier than ever, speeding once laborious, time-consuming hand operations.

### Get authentic plans

The first thing to do is obtain plans for the ship of your choice. This task is often easier than you may imagine. Contact the proper historical institution. If the ship is American, write directly to the Smithsonian Institution in Washington, D.C. Specify the ship you are looking for, and the Smithsonian is likely to have the original plans or duplicates on file. They will send you copies for a nominal fee. If they can't supply the plans you want, they will often refer you to a source that can.

Other sources for plans are hobby shops and maritime museums. Some hobby shops stock or can order plans for well-known historical vessels. If the ship you want is of foreign origin or an obscure design, your best bet may be a maritime museum. There are nearly 100 national maritime museums throughout the world. You can start by finding out where the ship you want was originally built, then write to the national maritime museum of that country. It will either have the plans or suggest other sources.

Plans will probably be in ⅛ or 3/16-in. scale. Beware of larger scale or you may find yourself with a model the size of your living room.

### Tools

Tools required for ship modeling are basically simple: a pair of needle-nosed pliers, cuticle scissors for fine cutting, a modeler's knife with a pointed blade, modeler's chisels, tweezers, a ¹⁄₃₂-in.-scale ruler, fine sandpaper and miniature electric hand drill or hand grinder. You can use a hobbyist's jigsaw for cutting out ribs, keel and other parts demanding precise accuracy. Use a small bench sander for shaping and finishing. If necessary, a coping saw can be substituted for the powered jigsaw and hand sanding for the bench sander.

### The building process

Working from original plans is relatively easy if you take them a step at a time and don't let yourself become confused by the mass of intricate detail. Take your time and study each part before attempting to reproduce it. Wherever possible, get pictures of the ship you're modeling.

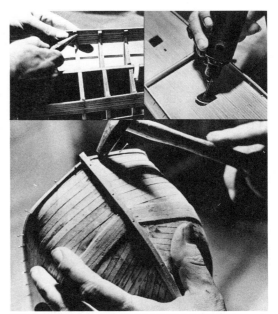

**MIGHTY THREE-MASTED SQUARE RIGGER,** shown in all her ornate glory on facing page, begins to take shape above. First step is planking hull. Thin wood strips, watersoaked to make them pliable, are glued and tacked on with brass pins as temporary fasteners. After glue sets, pins are removed with long-nosed pliers (top left) and holes "pegged." At top right, square holes for masts are formed in deck with tiny disc sander.

These will serve as an additional aid in deciphering the plans.

First step in the building process is to make precise tracings of the ribs and keel. These are then cut into templates, laid on ⅛-in.-thick plywood and traced again to produce the actual parts. The ribs and keel are cut out with a jigsaw or coping saw and matched against the original plan for accuracy.

Gluing begins when the keel and all ribs are cut. The ribs are slotted and glued along the keel at intervals specified by the plans.

The next step is to add planking. The planks are usually ¼ by 1/16-in. spruce or basswood, purchased from a hobby shop. These fine strips are attractive in color and grain and, because of their flexibility, are easy to apply to the curving contours of a wooden ship hull. The planks are treated in two stages. First the edges and ends are painted black so that when the strips are butted together, they're separated by thin black lines simulating the caulking between teak planks in traditional sailing ships. A quick way to do this is to tightly clamp the strips together in a stack and spray all the edges at one time with black lacquer.

Stage two is to separate the planks, let the paint dry, then soak them in a tub of water for two or three days. Soaking makes the wood pliable and easy to work. Begin planking by first laying a strip of wood in a straight line down one side of the hull, positioning it halfway between topside and the keel. This gives you a straight starting point for laying up the remaining planks. Glue the plank at each point where it meets a rib, using a water-soluble cement. At the same time, tack the plank in place with tiny ½-in. brass pins. These hold the plank until the glue dries. After applying the first strip, add others alternately on each side until the entire half of the hull is covered. Carefully trim the strips at the bow and stern. Then plank the opposite side of the hull in the same way. When all planks are applied, the

small brass pins are removed with needle-nosed pliers, leaving holes that are then drilled out and filled with tiny doweling "pegs" to simulate the pegged planking used in real sailing ships.

Careful hand-sanding with very fine paper smooths and tapers the hull, removing minor flaws in the planking and adding the graceful, sweeping contour lines typical of traditional square riggers. Planking the deck comes next and is done in much the same way as the sides of the hull, except the job is simpler and faster because there are usually no intricate contours involved.

### Finishing

The hull is finished in several steps, depending on the effect and appearance desired. Start with an overall coat of all-purpose sanding sealer, then follow with an oil-base wood stain rubbed on with a soft cloth. In some cases, wood trim is highlighted with paint, depending on historical accuracy or builder preference. Finally, the hull

**AUTHENTIC PLANS** of early sailing ships provide accurate data for superdetailed modeling. Copies of such originals are available at nominal cost from maritime museums and from historical institutions like the Smithsonian.

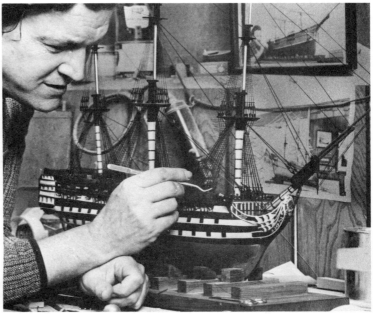

**MASTER MODELMAKER** (above) checks ''ratlins'' for proper tautness of rigging before putting finishing touches on a 17th-century British warship. Photos at left show fantastic detail and workmanship in masts, rigging and deck fittings that are typical of an authentic replica made from original ship's plans. Shown below is a unique method of mounting models. Instead of being held in a conventional cradle, the vessel sits on rows of wood blocks simulating heavy timbers, giving it the appearance of resting on ways ready for launching. Bolts that run through the keel hold it in place.

is given a second application of sanding sealer; this time it serves as a varnish to produce a softly gleaming satin finish.

### The display stand

With the hull completed, the ship is now ready for a stand. Instead of a conventional cradle or flat base, you can mount the hull between rows of small wood blocks fastened in turn to a plank. The blocks create the effect of a ship perched on the ways ready to be launched.

### Adding hull details

Hull detail begins with deck components such as hatches, winches, cabins, windlasses, capstans and transom. Here is where the use of pictures becomes an important supplement to the plans. While the plans will give the physical dimensions of such deck details, they will not show how they really looked. Many of these are highly distinctive and decorative in design, and only pictures can give you a true feeling of their appearance. The miniature woodwork is all made by hand. Tiny cabin windows are cut out with modeler chisels, hatch covers are shaped from thin spruce, lifeboats are carved from solid pine and winches are built up from a number of tiny individual pieces.

The transom, often the most ornate part of the ship, is usually a highly intricate arrangement of windows and scrollwork. Here's where a few special tricks, developed over years of experience, can be a valuable aid to the beginning modeler. In each carved opening for a window, dab a tiny spot of transparent glue and let it dry, forming a mottled pane of simulated glass. The result is amazingly realistic. For scrollwork and other textured effects, use liquid gesso, a surface-preparation material used by artists for oil paintings. When the fast-drying gesso is applied in repeated coats with a fine brush, it builds up a thick, irregular base that, when stained, takes on the appearance of intricately carved wood.

The technique can be used on figureheads, scrolls, flowers and other ornamental details. In fact, you can simply rough-cut your designs, then work them over with gesso to achieve the final results—like modeling with clay, but in miniature.

### Masts

Masts, yardarms, booms and bowsprits are all made from standard wood dowel stock. Select dowel diameters to match the fattest portions shown on the plans, then taper down the ends by eye. Do rough tapering on a bench sander and finish up with hand-sanding. Square holes for stepping masts are made by first drilling shallow round holes in the deck, then enlarging these into square openings with a disc sander chucked in a hand grinder.

### Rigging

Rigging is a subject in itself. Before trying it, a beginning ship modeler should study the technique thoroughly from readily available published sources.

Begin with the running rigging—the white lines that control the sails—and work upward. Once you get past the lower shrouds, the task is 75 percent complete. You can use Irish linen thread in varying weights depending on the ship's size. The ratlins, or ladder-type side rigging, are also of Irish linen thread and are rubbed generously with beeswax to stiffen them. Don't use synthetic nylon or rayon threads because they tend to stretch with time.

### Finishing details

Miniature metal fittings such as cannons, pulleys, chains and anchors are available ready-made for nearly every purpose on a ship. These can be obtained at, or ordered through, most hobby shops. While such items *can* be handmade—and a perfectionist would insist they should be—store-bought parts offer a handy way to avoid a lot of tedious work and are especially convenient for the beginner. It's no sin to add a few commercially made details if they'll improve the appearance of your handiwork. The important thing is the end result—and the thrill and satisfaction you'll get from turning out a masterpiece that's your very own from keel to crow's nest. And it's not all that hard, if you really want to do it.

# Scratch-built control-line airplanes

A

■ IF YOU HAVE a perfectly good model engine salvaged from the crash of a ready-to-fly plastic job, you can put it to work again powering one of these three easy-to-build control-line models made of balsa. Components such as bellcranks, elevator horns, wheels, tanks, lines and the like, are inexpensive and available at any hobby shop.

### VIGILANTE III

Building the Vigilente III is relatively simple. After studying the plans, shape and sand the fuselage sides from 1/8-in. balsa. Cut the plywood firewall and the balsa rear bulkhead and cement them to the fuselage sides with epoxy. Bend the landing gear from 1/16-in. wire, apply epoxy and sandwich the gear between the landing-gear mounts. Clamp in a vise until dry and epoxy to the fuselage. Next, shape, sand and hollow out the fuselage side blocks (1 x 1½ x 12 in.) and cement in place.

Cut the bellcrank platform from 1/8-in. plywood, epoxy the hardwood bellcrank to it (the top of a clothespin can be used for a mount) and attach the bellcrank with a screw.

**ENGINES**

Most small engines used to power ready-to-fly models can be easily adapted to homebuilt designs without modification. In some cases, flywheels must be removed and a new propeller added. Engines that have built-in fuel tanks (A) can be mounted directly to the firewall. Most current engines utilize miniature "glo plugs" for ignition which require a 1½-v. battery to start.

**ENGINE** with built-in fuel system (left) is mounted to firewall. Engine with separate fuel tank, rubber-banded to fuselage, bolts to side of fuselage.

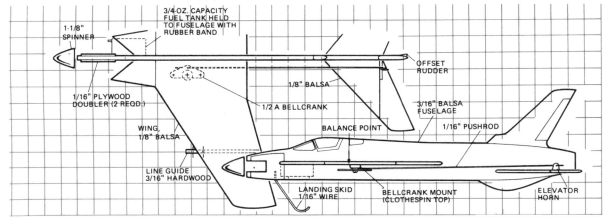

1-1/8" SPINNER

3/4-OZ. CAPACITY FUEL TANK HELD TO FUSELAGE WITH RUBBER BAND

OFFSET RUDDER

1/8" BALSA

1/16" PLYWOOD DOUBLER (2 REQD.)

1/2 A BELLCRANK

3/16" BALSA FUSELAGE

WING, 1/8" BALSA

BALANCE POINT

1/16" PUSHROD

LINE GUIDE 3/16" HARDWOOD

LANDING SKID 1/16" WIRE

BELLCRANK MOUNT (CLOTHESPIN TOP)

ELEVATOR HORN

Cement the wing in place, add the fuselage top sheeting and then the horizontal stabilizers. The elevators are connected with a ⅛-in. dowel and attached to the stabilizers with cloth hinges. Before hinging, epoxy the control horn to the left elevator. Attach the wire pushrod to the bell-crank and horn, cement the vertical stabilizer in place, offsetting the rudder as shown, and epoxy the hardwood line guide.

### Glue canopy to fuselage

After shaping and gluing together the cockpit canopy from four pieces of ⅛-in. balsa, glue it to the top of the fuselage. All that remains is to add the wheels which are held in place by collars and washers, and the engine which is attached to the firewall with four small screws.

Before cementing the wing and the horizontal and vertical stabilizers in place, cover them with Silkspun Coverite. It saves tedious filling and sanding and enables you to apply a good finish without the usual problems. Brush on several coats of clear dope, covering both sides, and when dry, sand each coat with No. 400 wet/dry sandpaper used dry. Now cement the wing in place, then the tail sections after first painting.

Apply three coats of clear dope to the rest of the plane and sand each with No. 220 sandpaper. Follow with four coats of sanding sealer, let dry for several days and sand again.

### Painting the model

Paint the upper half of the fuselage sides light gray, the lower half and the underside of the wing white. The cockpit windows are silver, the jet intakes black and the intake rims red. Add Navy decals. The panel lines are made with a pen. Protect the decals and panel lines from fuel damage with clear dope, spraying or brushing very lightly. Allow to dry for several days.

Tie a length of thread to a pin and press it into the fuselage at the balance point indicated. Raise the craft by the thread and add weight (wood scrap or light metal) to the nose or tail until the airplane hangs level. Never fly a plane that's tail-heavy.

Vigilente III is very stable in flight. On landing, anticipate when the engine will run out of fuel and take her down near the ground. The craft won't drop like a brick, but neither will it glide very far. It has a high sink rate.

### THE F-15

The F-15 is built basically the same. Start with the fuselage, install the formers, firewall and landing gear. The fuselage sides are made of 1/16-in.-thick sheet balsa. The canopy is from a Scientific or similar Mustang kit, and is blended into the fuselage with plastic balsa or a filler of your preference. Finally add the remaining essentials—engine, bell-crank, wire and control horn. Wing and tail surfaces are installed in the same way as the Vigilente III.

### THE F-105

The F-105 is simpler to build than the other two because it has a "profile" fuselage that requires no bulkheads, coverings and the like. The wing is cut from ⅛-in. balsa and brushed with several coats of clear dope. Apply it to both sides at a time to avoid warping. When dry, sand with No. 400 wet/dry sandpaper.

The fuselage is cut from 3/16-in. balsa and is notched where the wing goes. Cut the engine doublers from 1/16-in. plywood and epoxy them to the nose as shown. Cut the fuselage and doublers to fit your engine. The vertical stabilizer is cut from 3/16-in. balsa and can be either glued to the fuselage or be a part of the same piece. Cut the rudder and glue it into the offset shown. The ventral fin is cut from ⅛ or 3/16-in. balsa and glued to the bottom of the fuselage.

Cut the horizontal stabilizer and elevator from ⅛ or 3/16-in. balsa. Sand to shape and glue the stabilizer to the fuselage. Attach the elevator to the stabilizer with cloth hinges. Add the ⅛-in.-plywood horn to the elevator. Sand the edges of the fuselage, vertical stabilizer and ventral fin.

### Epoxy wing to fuselage

Install the wing to the fuselage with epoxy. Epoxy the bellcrank mount and the hardwood line guide, then the balsa tank-position guide.

Since the wing is already treated with clear dope, brush several coats on the fuselage and the rest of the model. Sand and camouflage the plane and install the engine. Lash on the ¾-oz. fuel tank with rubber bands. An optional wire landing skid can be added. Install the bellcrank and the wire.

Balance the plane as before, adding weight to nose or tail if needed. Hook up 25 to 35-ft. dacron flying lines. Before each flight, check the elevator for freedom of movement. On take-off have your helper run a few steps and then gently launch the plane. On landing, anticipate when the fuel will run out and fly straight and level. When the engine quits, glide the plane in and apply the up elevator just before touchdown.

Happy landings!

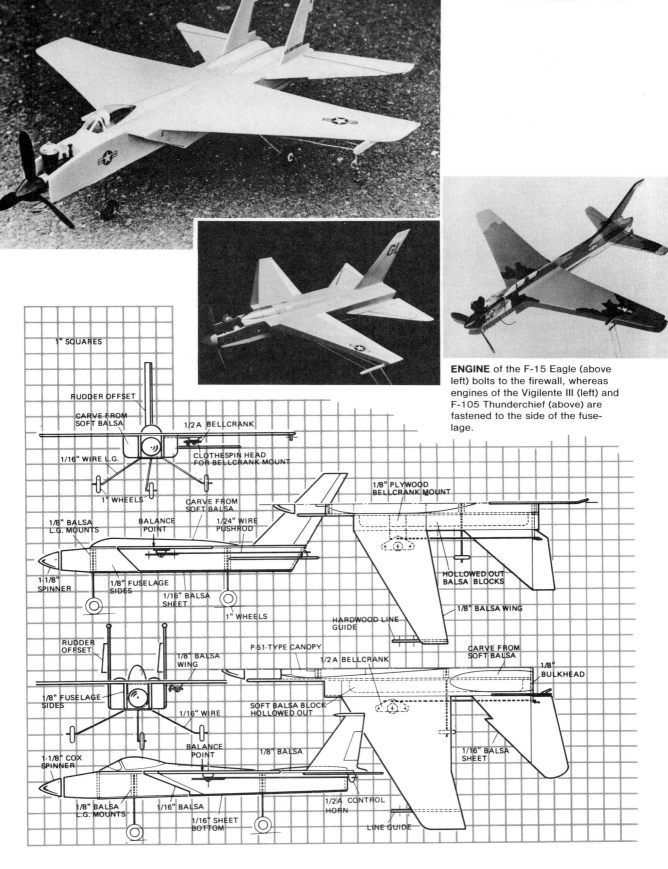

**ENGINE** of the F-15 Eagle (above left) bolts to the firewall, whereas engines of the Vigilente III (left) and F-105 Thunderchief (above) are fastened to the side of the fuse-lage.

1" SQUARES

RUDDER OFFSET

CARVE FROM SOFT BALSA

1/2A BELLCRANK

1/16" WIRE L.G.

CLOTHESPIN HEAD FOR BELLCRANK MOUNT

1" WHEELS

CARVE FROM SOFT BALSA

1/8" BALSA L.G. MOUNTS

BALANCE POINT

1/24" WIRE PUSHROD

1-1/8" SPINNER

1/8" FUSELAGE SIDES

1/16" BALSA SHEET

1" WHEELS

1/8" PLYWOOD BELLCRANK MOUNT

HOLLOWED OUT BALSA BLOCKS

1/8" BALSA WING

HARDWOOD LINE GUIDE

RUDDER OFFSET

1/8" BALSA WING

P-51-TYPE CANOPY

1/2A BELLCRANK

CARVE FROM SOFT BALSA

1/8" BULKHEAD

1/8" FUSELAGE SIDES

1/16" WIRE

SOFT BALSA BLOCK HOLLOWED OUT

1/16" BALSA SHEET

1-1/8" COX SPINNER

BALANCE POINT

1/8" BALSA

1/8" BALSA L.G. MOUNTS

1/16" BALSA

1/16" SHEET BOTTOM

1/2A CONTROL HORN

LINE GUIDE

# Moldings—the finishing touch

■ NO MATTER WHERE located, moldings are a basic of design, an element to be utilized in a wide range of applications. Without moldings almost any structure, anything with dimension, is little more than a box shape with stark overhangs and uninteresting square corners.

But a molding is a shape that catches the eye. It adds something both elemental and decorative, the finishing detail, leaves you with the feeling that the job is complete.

Traditional architecture utilizes a range of applied moldings both inside and outside the structure; inside as a finishing detail in a room, such as picture molding; a coved mold in the corner where wall meets ceiling; as a baseboard with quarter-round and as door and window trim with stops having one molded edge. Outside you see moldings in various forms under cornices, around sash frames and around and over door frames.

Common applied moldings are combinations of curves, reverse curves and plane surfaces generally worked on the face, corners and edges of both hard and softwood lumber. As a rule these shapes come in the form of strips varying in width and thickness and are sold by the lineal foot.

Common among the applied moldings are the simple cove and quarter-round shapes which are cut on small square or rectangular strips. The former shape is ordinarily used as trim under an overhanging member such as a mantel, shelf or similar application. The latter you'll see forming the trim where a baseboard meets flooring. Of course, there are variants in the application and shape of these forms which are commonly known as bed moldings.

Crown and cove moldings are similar in that both shapes are usually cut on one face of stock varying in width from 2 or 3 in. to 5 in. or more in the standard sizes.

As these moldings are usually intended to span a right-angle corner, as in a room where wall meets ceiling, the back corners are cut at a 45-deg. angle and the adjacent corners are trimmed at 90 deg. to the 45-deg. corners, the flats serving as "stops" for the curves cut on the face.

Cove moldings are commonly cut with a single concavity on the face, often the full width of the stock, but these also are cut in combinations of concavity and reverse curve, the former shape usually the wider of the two. A narrow plane surface, or flat, is usually cut between the shapes to serve as a stop at the ends of the curves.

Common crown moldings consist of variations of reverse-curve and cove cuts in combination on the same face of the stock. They come in standard widths from about 1½ in. up. Like the cove moldings, crown moldings in the larger sizes are designed to span a corner.

Half-round moldings, of which there are various sizes, generally are applied as nosings, that is, are nailed or otherwise fastened to square edges to serve either a practical or decorative purpose. On old work you will sometimes see half rounds attached to the outer edges of stair treads. Much the same is true of the combination half-round-and-cove mold which you will often find serving as a nosing on later-type stair treads. These usually have a half-round-and-cove shape cut on the same face of the strip. Such moldings generally come as strips ranging in widths from fractions of an inch to about 2 in. or more.

Stops commonly range in thickness from ⅜ to ½ in. and in widths up to 2 in. or more. These usually come with a reverse-curve molding on one corner but there also are variants of the shapes available. Some are supplied with only one corner slightly rounded to a uniform radius. Stops are used mainly in door and window

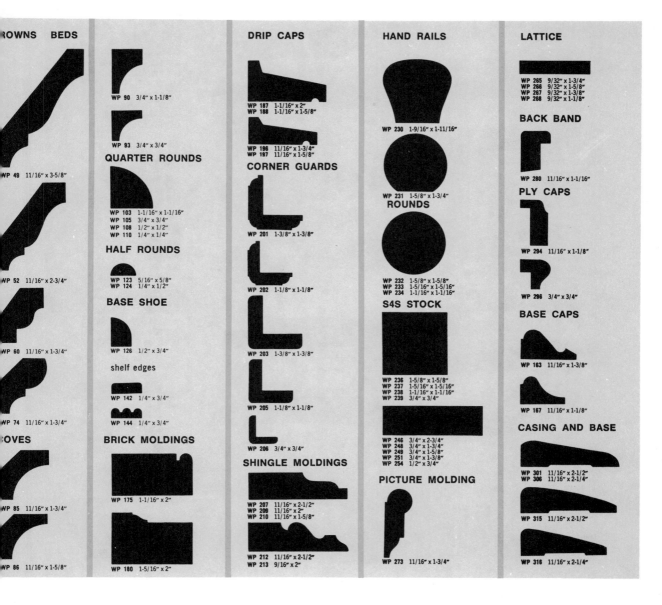

**ROWNS** **BEDS**

WP 49  11/16" x 3-5/8"

WP 52  11/16" x 2-3/4"

WP 60  11/16" x 1-3/4"

WP 74  11/16" x 1-3/4"

**OVES**

WP 85  11/16" x 1-3/4"

WP 86  11/16" x 1-5/8"

WP 90  3/4" x 1-1/8"

WP 93  3/4" x 3/4"

**QUARTER ROUNDS**

WP 103  1-1/16" x 1-1/16"
WP 105  3/4" x 3/4"
WP 108  1/2" x 1/2"
WP 110  1/4" x 1/4"

**HALF ROUNDS**

WP 123  5/16" x 5/8"
WP 124  1/4" x 1/2"

**BASE SHOE**

WP 126  1/2" x 3/4"

shelf edges

WP 142  1/4" x 3/4"

WP 144  1/4" x 3/4"

**BRICK MOLDINGS**

WP 175  1-1/16" x 2"

WP 180  1-5/16" x 2"

**DRIP CAPS**

WP 187  1-1/16" x 2"
WP 188  1-1/16" x 1-5/8"

WP 196  11/16" x 1-3/4"
WP 197  11/16" x 1-5/8"

**CORNER GUARDS**

WP 201  1-3/8" x 1-3/8"

WP 202  1-1/8" x 1-1/8"

WP 203  1-3/8" x 1-3/8"

WP 205  1-1/8" x 1-1/8"

WP 206  3/4" x 3/4"

**SHINGLE MOLDINGS**

WP 207  11/16" x 2-1/2"
WP 209  11/16" x 2"
WP 210  11/16" x 1-5/8"

WP 212  11/16" x 2-1/2"
WP 213  9/16" x 2"

**HAND RAILS**

WP 230  1-9/16" x 1-11/16"

WP 231  1-5/8" x 1-3/4"

**ROUNDS**

WP 232  1-5/8" x 1-5/8"
WP 233  1-5/16" x 1-5/16"
WP 234  1-1/16" x 1-1/16"

**S4S STOCK**

WP 236  1-5/8" x 1-5/8"
WP 237  1-5/16" x 1-5/16"
WP 238  1-1/16" x 1-1/16"
WP 239  3/4" x 3/4"

WP 246  3/4" x 2-3/4"
WP 248  3/4" x 1-3/4"
WP 249  3/4" x 1-5/8"
WP 251  3/4" x 1-3/8"
WP 254  1/2" x 3/4"

**PICTURE MOLDING**

WP 273  11/16" x 1-3/4"

**LATTICE**

WP 265  9/32" x 1-3/4"
WP 266  9/32" x 1-5/8"
WP 267  9/32" x 1-3/8"
WP 268  9/32" x 1-1/8"

**BACK BAND**

WP 280  11/16" x 1-1/16"

**PLY CAPS**

WP 294  11/16" x 1-1/8"

WP 296  3/4" x 3/4"

**BASE CAPS**

WP 163  11/16" x 1-3/8"

WP 167  11/16" x 1-1/8"

**CASING AND BASE**

WP 301  11/16" x 2-1/2"
WP 306  11/16" x 2-1/4"

WP 315  11/16" x 2-1/2"

WP 316  11/16" x 2-1/4"

framing and are ordinarily attached with small finishing nails having the heads set below the surface and the holes puttied flush. On the finest work the stops are attached with ovalhead screws, the heads being countersunk flush or turned down on plated washers.

Other shapes which classify as moldings are full rounds, screen moldings, chair rails, window stools and corner beads to name a few of the many shapes. Some of these are not so commonly used in present-day construction but most are still available as replacements. Full rounds in larger sizes are often utilized as stair rails. A variant (although it does not classify as mold-

ing) is the well-known dowel, which is regularly supplied 36 in. long.

If you've ever made screen frames you've used one of the several forms of screen moldings and you'll see many of the other forms illustrated in nearly all old work and occasionally in newer structures.

All the illustrations, which are end views of the shapes, show only one size. But, of course, many of the moldings come in several widths and thicknesses to adapt them to various types of work.

When installing moldings around outside corners the ends are mitered and it's the usual prac-

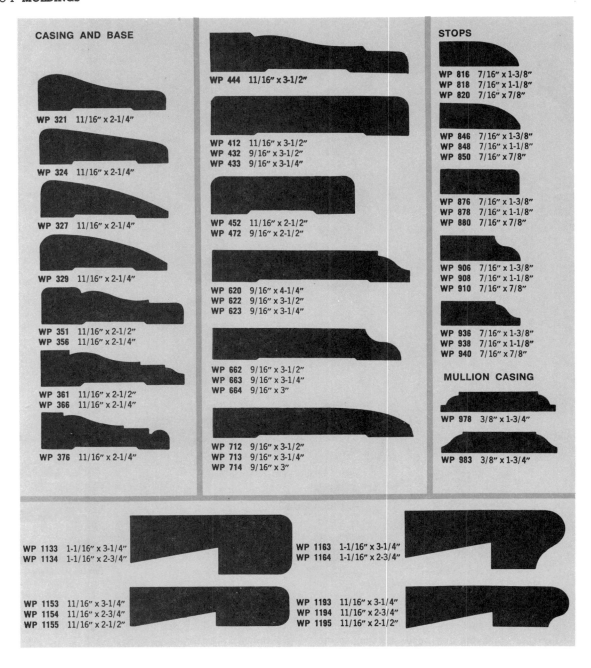

**CASING AND BASE**

WP 321    11/16" x 2-1/4"

WP 324    11/16" x 2-1/4"

WP 327    11/16" x 2-1/4"

WP 329    11/16" x 2-1/4"

WP 351    11/16" x 2-1/2"
WP 356    11/16" x 2-1/4"

WP 361    11/16" x 2-1/2"
WP 366    11/16" x 2-1/4"

WP 376    11/16" x 2-1/4"

WP 444    11/16" x 3-1/2"

WP 412    11/16" x 3-1/2"
WP 432    9/16" x 3-1/2"
WP 433    9/16" x 3-1/4"

WP 452    11/16" x 2-1/2"
WP 472    9/16" x 2-1/2"

WP 620    9/16" x 4-1/4"
WP 622    9/16" x 3-1/2"
WP 623    9/16" x 3-1/4"

WP 662    9/16" x 3-1/2"
WP 663    9/16" x 3-1/4"
WP 664    9/16" x 3"

WP 712    9/16" x 3-1/2"
WP 713    9/16" x 3-1/4"
WP 714    9/16" x 3"

**STOPS**

WP 816    7/16" x 1-3/8"
WP 818    7/16" x 1-1/8"
WP 820    7/16" x 7/8"

WP 846    7/16" x 1-3/8"
WP 848    7/16" x 1-1/8"
WP 850    7/16" x 7/8"

WP 876    7/16" x 1-3/8"
WP 878    7/16" x 1-1/8"
WP 880    7/16" x 7/8"

WP 906    7/16" x 1-3/8"
WP 908    7/16" x 1-1/8"
WP 910    7/16" x 7/8"

WP 936    7/16" x 1-3/8"
WP 938    7/16" x 1-1/8"
WP 940    7/16" x 7/8"

**MULLION CASING**

WP 978    3/8" x 1-3/4"

WP 983    3/8" x 1-3/4"

WP 1133    1-1/16" x 3-1/4"
WP 1134    1-1/16" x 2-3/4"

WP 1153    11/16" x 3-1/4"
WP 1154    11/16" x 2-3/4"
WP 1155    11/16" x 2-1/2"

WP 1163    1-1/16" x 3-1/4"
WP 1164    1-1/16" x 2-3/4"

WP 1193    11/16" x 3-1/4"
WP 1194    11/16" x 2-3/4"
WP 1195    11/16" x 2-1/2"

tice to cut the two members just lightly over at the mitered ends. This assures a tight fit (if the miter is properly cut, of course) and should there be slight shrinkage of the wood, or movement of the framing due to shrinkage, the mitered joint will remain a tight fit.

Moldings that meet in an inside corner should always be coped, that is, one member is cut and nailed in place the full length, the end in the corner being cut square off. Then the end of the meeting mold is cut to a shape that will fit tightly against the first member, using a scroll, or coping saw, and making the cut at a very slight angle. Moldings that fit between walls should not be forced; rather they should be cut slightly under.

# Work magic with moldings

■ THE NEXT TIME you plan to redecorate a room, pause a bit before deciding that a coat of paint or wallpaper is all you need to get a fresh look. With some planning, you will be pleasantly surprised at how dramatic a change can be achieved by simply adding wood moldings to the walls. Placing moldings on a flat wall surface is an inexpensive way to create a luxurious look.

Wood moldings are available in a large variety of styles and sizes at most lumberyards. The

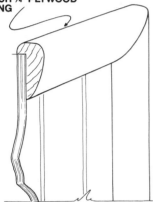

**PREFINISHED PLYCAP MOLDING TO MATCH ¼" PLYWOOD PANELING**

**PREFINISHED PLYWOOD**

**FRAMED** plywood panels have a look of luxury, yet cost less than a fully paneled wall. The plywood is glued to the wall, then surrounded with lengths of prefinished moldings.

11/16 x 1½"
PANEL MOLD

**MOLDING DETAILS** can be effectively used to set the period of design. To duplicate the room shown above, panels must be sized proportionately to suit the size of the wall.

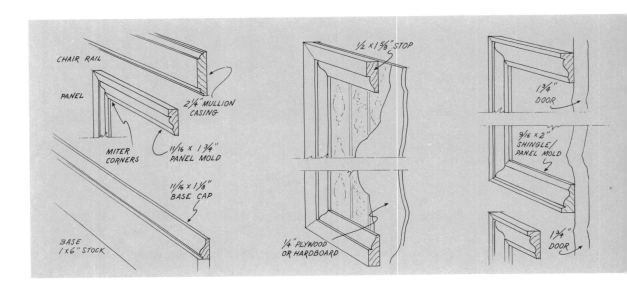

CHAIR RAIL

PANEL

MITER
CORNERS

2¼ MULLION
CASING

11/16 x 1¾"
PANEL MOLD

11/16 x 1⅛"
BASE CAP

BASE
1 X 6" STOCK

½ x 1⅝" STOP

¼" PLYWOOD
OR HARDBOARD

1¾"
DOOR

9/16 x 2"
SHINGLE/
PANEL MOLD

1¾"
DOOR

**PANELED WAINSCOTING** helps to reduce the feeling of height and emptiness along a stair wall.

rooms shown are good examples of what you can accomplish through thoughtful use of moldings. And when you have the know-how for working with this shaped stock, you'll be able to duplicate these examples more easily than you might suspect. The key to successful use of molding lies in careful planning.

Your first step should be a trip to your local lumberyard to learn which moldings it keeps in stock. Armed with this information, take the time to draw a scale floor plan and wall elevations of the room. To lay out a room such as the one above, the elevation drawing should indicate the chair rail at desired height (36 to 42 in.). Work out panel design and sizes so the wall will be symmetrical with panels balanced in height and width, and the spaces between panels equal.

The examples shown in photos and section drawings on these pages can be duplicated or can serve as a springboard for your own creative designs.

### Molding know-how

Make no mistake about it, your molding job will look only as good as the craftsmanship you put into it. How joints fit and nails are placed re-

**YOU CAN DRESS UP** an inexpensive flush door with wood moldings. Two versions—hung in the same opening—show how the moldings can change the look.

**ATTACH THE MOLDINGS** to an exterior door using waterproof glue and finishing nails. All 24 of the corner joints shown here were carefully mitered.

**FRESH, CRISP LOOK** is achieved by painting moldings to contrast with the walls. The chair rail not only looks good, but can be functional as well.

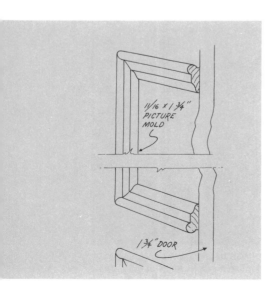

veal just how much effort was applied. The first rule is never to guess at miter cuts—always use a miterbox. Also, get in the habit of using sharp saws only. A dull saw—no matter how great your patience and effort—is almost certain to produce unsightly, amateurish-looking joints. Always place the piece of molding in the miterbox as it is to be installed on the wall. (It is important to remember this rule or you will waste a lot of molding by making miter cuts in the wrong plane.)

Because they tend to open, inside joints should always be coped as shown. Here, after cutting miter at desired point, use a coping saw held at a 45° angle, *a must on all convex moldings,* to create a back-cut. Follow the miter-cut profile to cut out this wedge and you'll have a perfect joint. A coped joint—like all molding joints—should be installed with glue as well as nails.

## HOW TO MITER AND COPE MOLDINGS

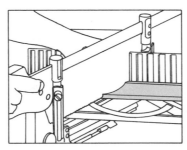

**SET MITER** box saw at 45° for miter cuts. Always hold molding securely while doing the cutting.

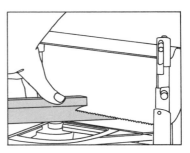

**TO COPE** a joint, first make the miter cut to the exact length desired as shown in diagram.

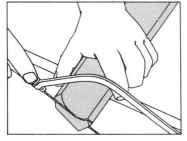

**NEXT,** with coping saw held at 45° angle, follow miter line (profile) to cut out wedge-shaped piece.

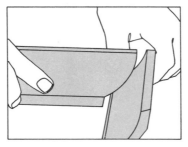

**TEST-FIT** the coped molding against piece of molding it will abut. In sequence shown, it's cove mold.

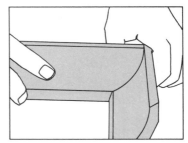

**YOU CAN** use a block plane and sandpaper to ensure a tight-fitting joint. Glue and nail to fasten.

## HOW TO DO BLIND NAILING

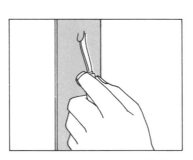

**CAREFULLY** gouge up a small sliver of wood that's wide enough to conceal the finishing-nail head.

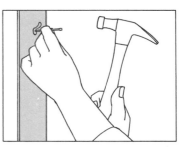

**SWING** the sliver carefully out of the way and drive the nail. Then set the nailhead well.

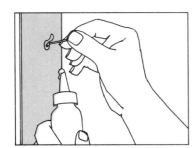

**APPLY** white glue to the sliver and push it into place. Immediately wipe off any glue ooze-out.

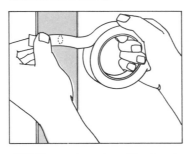

**PRESS** on a piece of masking tape to hold the sliver in place until the glue is completely dry.

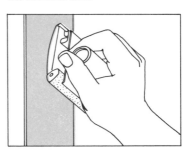

**AFTER** glue dries, remove masking tape and touch up the blind spot with a fine-grit sandpaper.

## WHERE MOLDINGS MEET AT RIGHT ANGLES

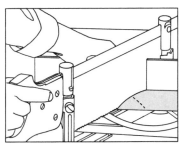

**TWO 45° CUTS** are made to create point with length equal to exactly half-width of the molding.

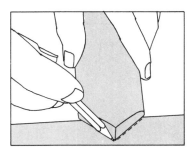

**USE THIS** piece as the layout pattern for cuts to be made on the piece it will join.

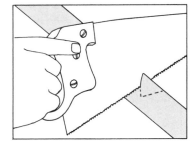

**FOLLOWING** the lines, use a fine tooth, crosscut saw to make the cutout on the mating molding.

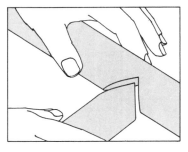

**CHECK** joint for fit. If you made the cuts carefully, joint should be practically invisible.

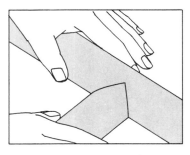

**WHEN** satisfied with the joint, use glue and toenail several brads through one mold into other.

# Period molding you can make

**REPRODUCE PERIOD** moldings from stock items available at lumberyards and home centers.

■ RECREATING AUTHENTIC PERIOD MOLDINGS *exactly* would be frustrating. But, by using stock lumber, you can closely duplicate the moldings of yesteryear.

### Baseboard

Shape the baseboard from 1×6 using a ¼-in. and ½-in. quarter-round molding head in a table saw. Make the first pass with the cutter tilted at 28°. Adjust the depth-of-cut so only the corner of the cutter projects above the table. Then readjust the cutter to the perpendicular position and make the second pass with the rounded portion of the molding head.

### Door surround

The trick to reproducing the gently curving S shape of the authentic door surround is to cut out the center of 2½-in. crown molding. Three cuts on a table saw are required to produce this piece. For the final cut, tack the center section temporarily to a scrap-wood guide. Rip remaining members for ¾-in. stock.

Make the jamb by first cutting a 45° bevel on one edge and then a shallow rabbet as shown. Finally, nail ¾-in. half-round molding to the bevel face.

### Cornice

Make the cornice from 3½-in. crown molding and a ¾×¾-in. piece. Rabbet the piece to fit molding. Nail the cornice where ceiling and walls meet. Butt top of the molding to ceiling.

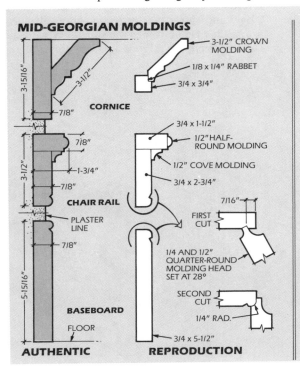

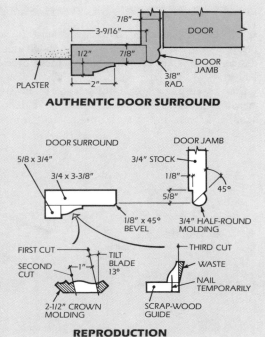

**HOLDER KEEPS** cutters sharp. It can be stowed in a drawer. Use a dado head (right) on a radial-arm saw or a table saw to plow the grooves and dadoes. Tilt saw's head 15° to create the slightly angled dadoes.

# Molding cutter storage

■ LOOSE CUTTERS, banging around in a drawer with other tools, are easily dulled and damaged. This cutter holder solves these problems.

Start by cutting a 1 1/16-in.-thick board to the dimensions given in the materials list. Set a dado head 5/8-in. wide and at a 15° angle to cut 3/4-in.-deep dadoes. Rotate workpiece and reset saw to 90° and the dado head for cutting the 1/4-in. grooves, 3/4 in. deep. Use marks at the edges of the base (A) to locate the cuts.

Now cut divider strips (C) slightly higher and longer than the grooves into which they are to be inserted. Also cut the sidepieces (B) slightly longer and higher than required. Apply glue, assemble and clamp. When the glue is dry, sand all surfaces flush for a good-looking project.

## MATERIALS LIST

| Key | No. | Size and description |
|-----|-----|----------------------|
| A | 1 | 1 1/16x5 1/4x9″ hardwood |
| B | 2 | 1/4x1 1/8x9 1/16″ hardwood |
| C | 3 | 1/4x$^{13}$/16x9 1/16″ hardwood |

**Misc.:** White glue, polyurethane.

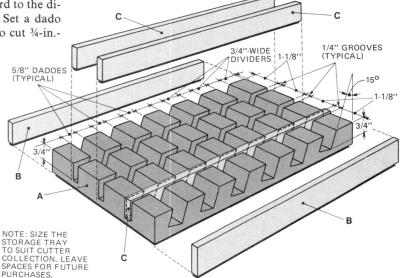

NOTE: SIZE THE STORAGE TRAY TO SUIT CUTTER COLLECTION. LEAVE SPACES FOR FUTURE PURCHASES.

# Electric motors—a guide

■ WHEN YOU NEED a replacement motor for an appliance or workshop tool, ordering a new unit is easy enough—just take the necessary data from the motor's nameplate. But when you're scratch-building a worksaver like a bench saw, don't make the common mistake of selecting a motor by simply guessing.

Actually there are four factors you must consider before making a choice: horsepower rating, starting effort, shaft speed and operating voltage.

Horsepower is the primary consideration. As an indication of requirements for different jobs, the table on the next page lists motors of various horsepower and their typical uses. If your particular application is not listed, simply compare it to a similar job and select the next larger motor to avoid overloading.

Continual overloading of a motor above its rated power can cause it to overheat and shorten its life. For this reason, most new fan, blower, pump, compressor and conveyor motors have automatic-reset overload protection to guard against such overheating. It's important that the

thermal protector automatically resets the motor in installations like a furnace blower, where you would not want the furnace to remain inoperative overnight, or on water pumps located away from the house. A manual-reset overload device, however, is recommended for motors that drive potentially dangerous tools, such as a saw, jointer or lathe.

Load moving is critical when you start a motor. Machines such as free-running saws or fans are easy to start. Others that must start under load—such as concrete mixers, conveyors, pumps and air compressors—need motors with extra turning strength, or torque, during the starting revolutions. For most home, farm and workshop uses, easy-to-start machines call for *split-phase* motors; hard-to-start machines require *capacitor-start* motors.

Split-phase motors have only moderate starting torque and are built with ratings up to ⅓ hp. Two windings, start and run, are energized at first. At about 80 percent of operating speed, a centrifugal switch cuts the start winding out of the circuit.

Capacitor-start motors, on the other hand, deliver two to three times the starting torque for the same amount of current. These are made with ratings from ⅙ to 3 hp. Since capacitor-start motors cost from 25 to 50 percent more than split-phase motors of like power, split-phase is the logical choice when the starting load is light (as on fans and blowers), or where the load is applied after the motor reaches full operating speed (drill press).

Both types use a single-phase power supply and, combined, make up about 90 percent of the motors in the U.S. Polyphase (usually three-phase) motors constitute the balance and are designed for continuous heavy-duty work. Because of the three-phase power requirement, however, polyphase motors are not often found in home workshops.

Most single-phase motors run at full load speeds of either 1725 or 3450 rpm. The faster motor is frequently the smaller of the two, and has a lower price per hp. When possible, this is the type to use since its speed can be reduced by a 6:1 belt-and-pulley combination.

With regard to voltage, a look at the motor's nameplate will tell you whether its rating corresponds to your power supply, which likely is 115 v.a.c., 60 cycle. The dual-voltage (115/230-v.), capacitor-start motors are available with ratings beginning at ⅙ hp, while split-phase motors are rated at ⅙ hp through ½ hp.

## COMMON USES FOR ELECTRIC MOTORS

| APPLICATION | HORSEPOWER | SPEED | MOTOR TYPE |
|---|---|---|---|
| Belt sander, 4″ | ¼ | 1725 | Split-phase |
| Belt sander, 6″ | ½ | 1725 | Capacitor-start |
| Belt sander, 10″ | 1 | 1725 | Capacitor-start |
| Belt-driven blower | ⅛-¾ | 1725 | Split-phase |
| Churn | ⅓ | 1725 | Split-phase |
| Small compressor | ⅙-¾ | 1725 | Capacitor-start |
| Small concrete mixer | ½ | 1725 | Capacitor-start |
| Cream separator | ½ | 1725 | Capacitor-start |
| Drill press, ¼″ | ⅓ | 1725 | Split-phase |
| Drill press, ½″ | ½ | 1725 | Capacitor-start |
| Drill press, ¾″ | ¾ | 1725 | Capacitor-start |
| Belt-driven fan | ⅛-¾ | 1725 | Split-phase |
| Feed mixer, 15-bushel | ¾ | 1725 | Capacitor-start |
| Feed grinder | ¾ | 1725 | Capacitor-start |
| Flexible shaft, 5/16″ dia. x 50′ | ⅓ | 1725 | Split-phase |
| Flexible shaft, ½″ dia. x 75′ | ½ | 1725 | Capacitor-start |
| Wheel grinder, 6″ | ⅓ | 1725 | Split-phase |
| Wheel grinder, 7″ | ½ | 1725 | Split-phase |
| Wheel grinder, 8″ | 1 | 1725 | Capacitor-start |
| Jigsaw, 12 or 15″ | ¼ | 1725 | Split-phase |
| Jigsaw, 18 or 25″ | ⅓ | 1725 | Split-phase |
| Jointer, 4½″ | ½ | 3450 | Capacitor-start |
| Jointer, 6″ | ½ | 3450 | Capacitor-start |
| Jointer, 8″ | ¾ | 3450 | Capacitor-start |
| Lathe (metal), 6″-swing | ½ | 1725 | Capacitor-start |
| Lathe (metal), 10″-swing | ¾ | 1725 | Capacitor-start |
| Lathe (wood), 8″-swing | ⅓ | 1725 | Split-phase |
| Lathe (wood), 12″-swing | ¾ | 1725 | Capacitor-start |
| Small meat grinder | ¼ | 1725 | Split-phase |
| Oil burner | ⅛-¼ | 1725 | Split-phase |
| Small paint sprayer | ⅓ | 1725 | Capacitor-start |
| Planer | ¾ | 3450 | Capacitor-start |
| Jet pump | ⅓-2 | 3450 | Capacitor-start |
| Sump pump | ⅓ | 1725 | Split-phase |
| Pump jack | ½ | 1725 | Capacitor-start |
| Bandsaw, 8″ throat | ⅓ | 1725 | Capacitor-start |
| Bandsaw, 10, 12 or 14″ | ½ | 1725 | Capacitor-start |
| Bench saw, 6 or 7″ | ½ | 3450 | Capacitor-start |
| Bench saw, 8″ | ¾ | 3450 | Capacitor-start |
| Bench saw, 10″ | 1 | 3450 | Capacitor-start |
| Spindle shaper | ½ | 3450 | Capacitor-start |
| Stoker | ⅓ | 1725 | Capacitor-start |

# Home workshop motor repair

**LOOK FOR** a small setscrew at the base of the pulley and tighten it with an Allen wrench.

■ HOME WORKSHOP MOTORS, the kind you use to run table saws and drill presses, are among the most reliable machines in your home. With modest care, such motors will give years and years of trouble-free service. The care involves nothing more than a few drops of oil each month if the motor has oil cups, and brushing dust and dirt and sawdust off it.

If you took the case off of the typical workshop motor, you'd see an armature consisting of copper wires wound around a cylindrical rotor; and field coils of copper wire inside of which the armature turns. The armature and field coils are connected by carbon elements called brushes mounted in the commutator, an assembly of copper bars around one end of the armature shaft. One brush is positive and the other is negative. They are directly opposite each other, and are held in firm contact with the commutator by springs.

Thus the armature on its shaft is the motor's only moving part (except for the carbon brushes which push against the commutator). One reason for the great dependability of the workshop motor is the fact that it has very few moving parts.

Here are some of the more common failures that occur in workshop motors:

*1. A loose pulley.* The pulley, of course, is not a part of the motor itself but is attached to the armature shaft. It is slipped over the end of the shaft and held in place by tightening a set screw. See the photograph above. If this setscrew loosens, the pulley may wobble or even work its way off the shaft. To avoid unexpected problems, check the setscrew occasionally. If it should be loose, tighten it by using an Allen wrench of the correct size. (If you don't have one, you can buy an inexpensive set of common-sized Allen wrenches at your home center.)

While you are inspecting the pulley, you should also check the drive belt. Belts are subject to wear and they may harden and crack with age. They also may stretch slightly so they're loose on the pulley. Test the belt by pressing down on it with your finger. You should be able to depress the belt about half an inch with moderate finger pressure. If it depresses more than that, the belt should be tightened. If you note cracks or badly worn places on the belt, replace it. To be sure of getting the correct replacement, take the old belt with you to the store.

*2. A loose wire.* If you find that your motor sometimes starts and sometimes does not, or if it emits sparks, you can suspect a loose wire. There are only a couple of wires which can be loose, and these are located, as a rule, under a cover plate you will find on one end of the motor. The cover plate is held in place by two small screws. Remove these.

Before removing the cover plate, unplug or disconnect the motor from the electric power

**THE ACCESS PLATE** on the end panel of the housing can be removed to tighten electrical connections.

**WITH THE PLATE OFF,** you have a clear view of any loose wires and can tighten all connections.

source. With the cover plate off, you can use a small wrench to tighten the connections. Then replace the plate and reconnect the motor.

*3. Bad brushes.* The brushes in a motor are small pieces of carbon held under spring tension against the turning commutator. They are subject to wear and may have to be replaced every few months in a motor which gets an exceptional amount of use, or perhaps every few years in a motor which gets only occasional use.

You can suspect worn brushes when the motor starts sluggishly or gives off sparks as it runs. Some motors have brushes contained in small housings under slotted caps. By carefully removing these caps, you can replace the brushes without disassembling the motor.

When removing these caps, turn slowly and lift away slowly, because the brushes under the caps are spring loaded. If you pull the cap away suddenly, the spring and the brush will fly out. Lift the cap slowly, allowing the spring under it to relax. Then lift the spring and brush out.

Check the spring as well as the brush, and replace both if necessary. You can buy springs and brushes at good hardware stores or at places which specialize in home power tools. To install the new brushes, simply insert them in the chamber under the cap, put the spring into the chamber, and then screw the cap into place. Always replace both brushes, positive and negative, at the same time.

In some motors, you must disassemble the motor housing to get at the brushes. Begin the disassembly by removing the pulley from the shaft. Then look for screwheads in indentations on the side of the housing. The housing is held together by long screws which extend through the motor. As a rule, there are four screws, secured by nuts at the other end. Use a screwdriver to remove these screws, being careful to hold the nuts as the screws are loosened.

With the screws removed, you should be able to lift away both ends of the motor housing. If the ends stick, place a block of wood against each of them and tap it briskly with a hammer until the component loosens.

With the ends of the motor housing removed, you should see the brush holders at the commutator end of the armature shaft. The brush holders may be held in place by small screws or clips. Remove these and lift each holder off the motor, then remove from it the brush and brush spring.

As before, check the brush and the spring and replace both as necessary. Also, replace both the positive and negative brushes. Insert the new brush and spring in the holder, then put the holder back in position on the motor with the tip of the brush in contact with the commutator.

*4. Frozen bearings.* Fortunately, bearings don't fail very often. The usual cause is lack of lubrication. Keep in mind that there are two kinds of motors in terms of lubrication. There are those which are lubricated at the factory and sealed, and never require any additional lubrication. And there are others which have tiny oil cups built in just over the main drive shaft. These little oil cups have spring-loaded caps on them to keep them closed, keeping dirt out. If your motor has these little cups, you must add several drops of machine oil regularly. If the cups run dry and the motor continues to run, you are risking frozen, burned-out bearings.

If the bearings burn out, you face an expensive repair job, one which you shouldn't attempt to do yourself. The professional mechanic and motor specialist has special pullers for removing bearings from the end cap. Without these special tools, you can easily ruin an otherwise repairable motor. Some do-it-yourselfers try to remove the end cap with a hammer to get at the bearings. It may work, but the risk of a ruined motor is great.

You sometimes can tell that the bearings are going bad when the motor begins to run noisily. In time, the bearings will freeze: The motor will hum when you turn it on, but it will not revolve. When that happens, remove the motor from the tool and take it to a professional repairman.

*Operating tips.* Keep in mind that the home workshop motor is a split-phase motor and that, as such, it draws a heavy electric current as it starts and for the first 10 seconds of operation.

This is the reason that the lights in your workshop may dim momentarily when you start a motorized unit.

Under normal circumstances, this overload doesn't mean anything to the average homeowner. But there are two times when it can be very important.

One time is when all the current is shut off in the house as, for example, when the power company shuts down the power for an hour or two to make repairs. When the power is turned on again, everything electrical with its switch turned on starts immediately. If several motor-powered units are on—say the furnace blower, the washer, the dryer, and the refrigerator—all of these motors will be activated at the same time. This causes a great drain of power, since all of these motors draw so heavily in the first few seconds, and the usual result is a bevy of blown fuses.

The other time the heavy power drain caused by the starting of a home workshop motor is important is when you are operating several power tools on the same electric circuit. The electric circuit in your workshop is (or should be) a 20-amp. circuit, capable of carrying 2300 watts.

It is a good idea to know the wattage of each tool and accessory in your workshop, and to keep a mental total of how many watts you are drawing at any time. This way, you can anticipate overload problems.

**THE MOTOR** housing is held together by long screws and nuts. Remove the screws to disassemble.

**PULL THE ENDS** of the motor housing apart to gain access to the brush holders on the commutator.

**SECRET** of the unique setup is that the large pulley (lower left) is free-running on the motor shaft.

**BRONZE BUSHING** (below) is epoxied to a ½-in. motor shaft to enlarge the bearing surface for pulley.

**PIGGYBACK SETUP** (below right) is ideal for cramped quarters, such as making your bandsaw a metalcutter.

# Piggyback speed reducer

■ LIFT YOURSELF by your bootstraps?

That's what this novel piggyback speed reducer appears to do, for it cuts your 1725-rpm double-shaft motor to under 200 rpm, and with only *one* shaft.

The heart of the speed reducer is the 6-in. free-running pulley to which the drive pulley is bolted. It revolves freely and is driven through speed-reducing pulleys from the other end of the motor. To use the motor at normal speed, you just slip one belt and turn a setscrew.

To construct the piggyback, remove the top motor-housing bolts and replace the longer bolts. Sections of angle iron, shimmed out with spacers of ⅛-in. pipe, provide support for the hangers.

Many ½-in. motor shafts have a flat ground on the shaft. In this case epoxy a ½-in. bronze bushing over the shaft and use a ⅝-in. arbor pulley.

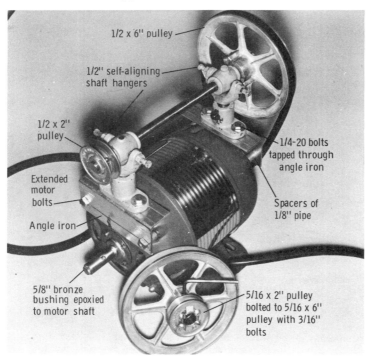

1/2 x 6" pulley

1/2" self-aligning shaft hangers

1/2 x 2" pulley

Extended motor bolts

Angle iron

1/4-20 bolts tapped through angle iron

Spacers of 1/8" pipe

5/8" bronze bushing epoxied to motor shaft

5/16 x 2" pulley bolted to 5/16 x 6" pulley with 3/16" bolts

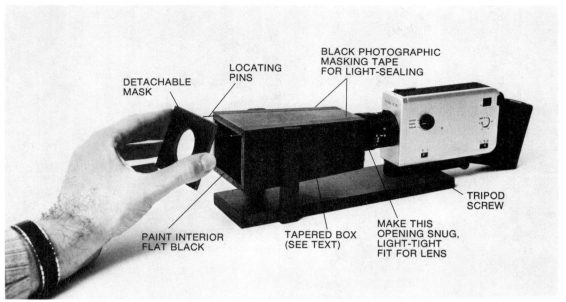

DETACHABLE MASK

LOCATING PINS

BLACK PHOTOGRAPHIC MASKING TAPE FOR LIGHT-SEALING

TRIPOD SCREW

PAINT INTERIOR FLAT BLACK

TAPERED BOX (SEE TEXT)

MAKE THIS OPENING SNUG, LIGHT-TIGHT FIT FOR LENS

**CONSTRUCTION IS SIMPLE,** but the dimensions must be adapted to the particular lens and camera model.

# Frame movies with a matte box

■ USING SOME NEARBY OBJECTS to put a frame around your movie shots can make a good shot even better, by adding depth and atmosphere to a pretty scene that might otherwise look flat and dull on your screen. Look carefully, and you'll find suitable objects all around you—overhanging trees, picturesque archways, portholes, windows—the list is limited only by your imagination, by what the subject of your particular shot calls for, and by the location of these natural frames.

But often the right object to silhouette in your foreground isn't quite in the right place to frame your subject. And sometimes you may want to spice a shot with a frame not naturally on the scene—a keyhole, perhaps, or the overlapping circles of movie "binoculars" (real binoculars, of course, show more of a fuzzy oval than the sharp figure-8 pattern the movies show you).

Professional filmmakers always have the frames they need, though, whenever they need them. Their frames are small cutouts called "mattes," attached to their cameras with simple devices called "matte boxes." The effect is quite professional—but the construction of a matte box is so simple that you can easily build your own.

It's basically just a tapered, light-tight box painted black inside, with a round hole at its small end to admit the camera lens, and provision for mounting interchangeable framing masks over the other end. Dimensions vary from camera to camera. The small end of the box should be just large enough to admit the front of your lens.

The dimensions of the other end will depend upon the type of lens you have: With a zoom lens, you should be able to see the edges of any mask in your finder when the lens is set to its shortest focal length, yet be unable to see the mask when the lens is zoomed to its telephoto position. With a nonzoom lens, you want the edges of the mask to be visible when the mask is mounted, but for the edges of the mattebox to be out of the frame when the mask is off. The mask size also depends on the length of the box—and the length must be a compromise; the longer you make it, the more sharply outlined your matte frame will be—but

**THE VARIETY OF MATTES** is unlimited. Besides these, others could be cut from photos of trees or other subjects.

the more ungainly and harder to handle the box will be, too.

Both the top and sides of the box should taper evenly and symmetrically, and the box's cross section should be a rectangle, approximately three quarters as high as it is wide.

With most cameras, the box will have to sit on struts above the baseboard, as this one does; again, the height of the struts depends on the camera. You can make your box from ¼-inch hardboard, plywood, opaque plastic, or what have you. Suitable scraps of wood can usually be picked up from lumber yards for a song. For the

base, use ½-inch lumber. Drill the base below the tripod-screw socket, and let your tripod's screw hold both the camera and the box assembly.

The mattes themselves can be cut from ⅛-inch hardboard, wood, cardboard, or similar material. Four ¾-inch brads in the corners of the box's "window" end mate with small holes in the matte's corners to hold them in place.

To finish, tape the corners of the box with black photographic tape to prevent light leaks, and kill interior reflections by painting the inside of the box with flat black paint.

A few of the possible effects are shown above.

# Hideaway home theater

■ BY THE TIME you haul out all the gear required to put on a slide or movie show, a lot of the fun has gone for you and your guests. This hideaway wall unit is designed to end the fuss and put the fun back into showing slides and movies. There's no screen to get out and set up because it's already built into the unit—you just pull it down and slip the projector out of one of the side cabinets.

When the screen is not in use, it disappears up into a recess at the top and is completely hidden from view. In its place are shelves for displaying decorative objects, giving the unit an attractive appearance when it's not serving as an instant home theater. The cabinets, besides storing photographic gear, can also house hi-fi equipment, making the unit an all-around home entertainment center. The cabinets are spaced apart

**WITH THE SCREEN RETRACTED** (above), the unit looks like an ordinary wall cabinet with storage cupboards and knickknack shelves. Conversion to home theater (below) takes only seconds, makes showing slides or movies fun instead of a nuisance. The unit can be anchored to wall or suspended on shelf brackets.

just right for good stereo listening from small book-shelf-type speakers placed inside the cupboards. The doors have mesh-covered openings designed to let sound through.

If you go in for sound movies or sound-synced slide shows, the setup is ideal because the accompanying sound, filtering out through the mesh doors, will appear to come right from the projection screen. For added convenience, you can install a flush-mounting music/intercom system, as shown on page 2004. These systems come in a variety of types and price ranges and offer a complete home communication center in a single, smartly styled unit with built-in radio, speaker and intercom controls.

The wall unit is built around a 40x40-inch pull-down screen. This type is designed expressly for wall or ceiling mounting and has brackets on the case that permit the screen to be hung from hooks or attached with screws. Such screens cost about the same as the regular floor-stand type.

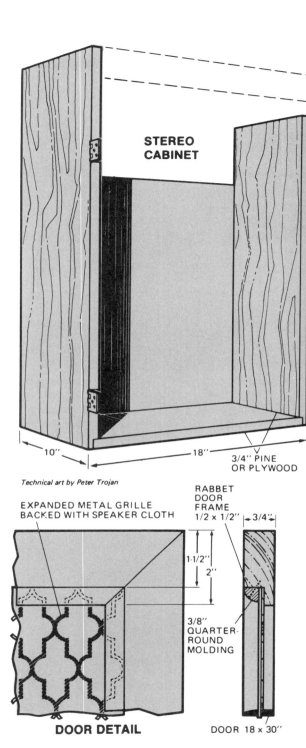

**STEREO CABINET**

10″  18″  3/4″ PINE OR PLYWOOD

Technical art by Peter Trojan

EXPANDED METAL GRILLE BACKED WITH SPEAKER CLOTH

RABBET DOOR FRAME 1/2 x 1/2″  3/4″

1-1/2″  2″

3/8″ QUARTER-ROUND MOLDING

**DOOR DETAIL**  DOOR 18 x 30″

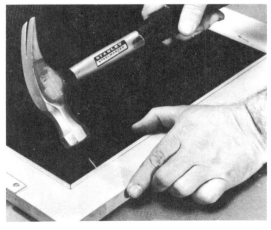

**GRILLE-COVERED OPENINGS** in doors are designed to let sound through even when the doors are closed. Door rails are rabbeted to form recess on back side, then decorative brass mesh is trimmed with tin snips to fit inside (top photo at left). The mesh is backed with black speaker cloth, and both are held in place with ⅜-inch quarter-round molding strips tacked in with small brads.

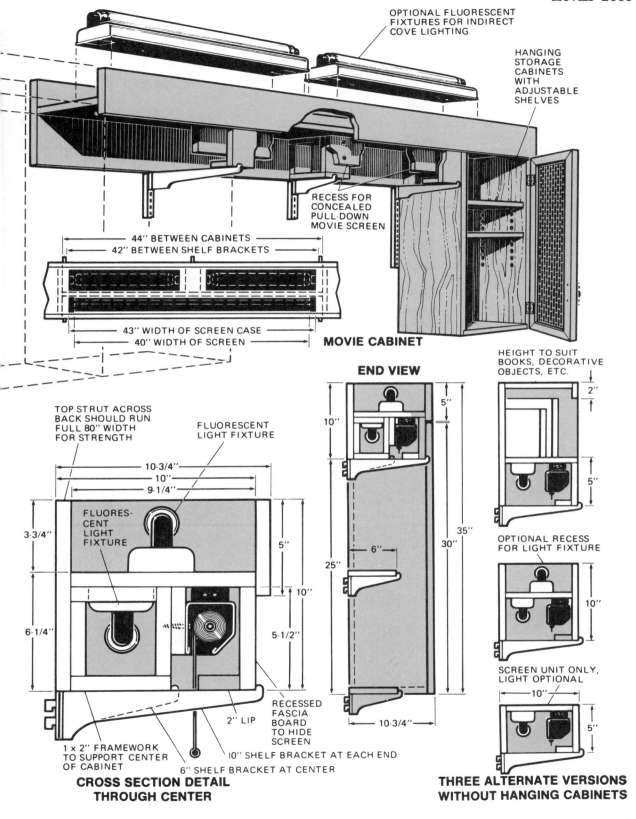

OPTIONAL FLUORESCENT FIXTURES FOR INDIRECT COVE LIGHTING

HANGING STORAGE CABINETS WITH ADJUSTABLE SHELVES

RECESS FOR CONCEALED PULL-DOWN MOVIE SCREEN

44" BETWEEN CABINETS
42" BETWEEN SHELF BRACKETS

43" WIDTH OF SCREEN CASE
40" WIDTH OF SCREEN

**MOVIE CABINET**

**END VIEW**

HEIGHT TO SUIT BOOKS, DECORATIVE OBJECTS, ETC.

2"

5"

TOP STRUT ACROSS BACK SHOULD RUN FULL 80" WIDTH FOR STRENGTH

FLUORESCENT LIGHT FIXTURE

10-3/4"
10"
9-1/4"

3-3/4"

FLUORES-CENT LIGHT FIXTURE

5"

6-1/4"

10"

5-1/2"

5"

OPTIONAL RECESS FOR LIGHT FIXTURE

10"

10"

6"

25"

35"

30"

RECESSED FASCIA BOARD TO HIDE SCREEN

2" LIP

SCREEN UNIT ONLY, LIGHT OPTIONAL

10"

5"

1 x 2" FRAMEWORK TO SUPPORT CENTER OF CABINET

10" SHELF BRACKET AT EACH END

6" SHELF BRACKET AT CENTER

10-3/4"

**CROSS SECTION DETAIL THROUGH CENTER**

**THREE ALTERNATE VERSIONS WITHOUT HANGING CABINETS**

FLUORESCENT LIGHT FIXTURE

Dimensions of the unit can be altered as desired, but the 10-inch depth was chosen because it enables all parts except the back panels to be ripped from stock 1x12-inch lumber with little waste. The unit can be screwed directly to the wall, just as you would mount a kitchen cabinet, or it can be supported on metal shelf brackets of the type that hook into slotted wall standards. The 10-inch depth enables the unit to fit perfectly on standard 10-inch-long shelf brackets.

If you decide on wall brackets, one construction pointer is important. The unit should be supported on no fewer than *three* brackets—one at each end and one at the middle. The center bracket can't extend the full cabinet depth, however, or it would obviously block the screen from coming down. The answer here is to build up a small supporting framework at the center of the span just behind the screen. This framework is 6 inches deep and rests on a 6-inch shelf bracket, supporting the middle of the unit without interfering with the operation of the screen. The knickknack shelves also rest on 6-inch brackets, providing sufficient clearance for the screen to pull down in front.

For maximum strength, the main strut running across the back at the top should extend the full 80-inch width—behind the cabinets as well

**HANGING SIDE CABINETS** can house various pieces of equipment depending on your needs. Here, one is fitted with an in-a-wall music/intercom system designed to mount in shallow spaces. Upper unit (below left) is AM/FM radio with 10-station intercom. Lower unit is fold-up record changer that swings out horizontally for use (center). Opposite cabinet (right) holds a Super-8 movie projector, film reels and a speaker.

**UNDERSIDE VIEW** with fascia board removed shows how the screen mounts at top of the unit between cabinets. With fascia board in place, the screen is hidden from view. Screen shown here is a 40 x 40-inch model. Two-way end brackets permit it to be hung from hooks or attached with screws.

as the screen—since it supports the entire weight of the unit where hung on shelf brackets. If you plan to mount the unit directly on the wall, you can, of course, eliminate the strut and center supporting framework.

Other options and variations are possible, too. As shown here, the unit incorporates a recess at the top for installing fluorescent lighting fixtures. These provide a soft, pleasing cove lighting effect. You can also build just the screen enclosure without the hanging side cabinets. Several alternate versions of this type are shown.

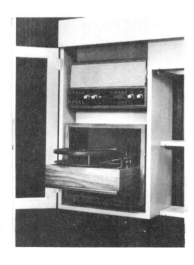

# Get your power mower ready for spring

## CLEAN COOLING FINS

The engine of a power mower is cooled by circulating air through fins inside the blower housing. If these fins become clogged and the airflow is blocked, the cooling process will be impeded or stopped completely. Overheating and damage to the internal parts can and will result. To clean the cooling fins, remove the blower housing and use a clean, dry paintbrush to brush dirt from between the fins. Packed-in dirt first can be loosened with a screwdriver.

If dirt is stubborn, use a commercial degreaser and a narrow, stiff-bladed scraper to clean out the fins. Fins should be cleaned periodically during the season.

CLEAN UNDERSIDE OF BLADE HOUSING

## THEN CLEAN UNDERSIDE OF BLADE HOUSING

Often, because grass is moist when cut, the underside of the blade housing becomes clogged with layers of dried-on grass. If you failed to turn the mower over and clean the blade housing with a putty knife and whiskbroom after each cutting session, the task will be somewhat harder now. After each cleaning, also turn the machine right-side up and wipe the body exterior with a soft, clean cloth. A spray automotive-engine degreaser can be used to dissolve stubborn dirt and grease.

Now pay special attention to the carburetor linkage and choke-plate pivots. To clean these units, use a spray-type automotive-carburetor cleaner that's available at auto supply outlets. Then apply a drop of oil to the moving parts. Finally, remove the wheels, thoroughly clean the hubs and axles, and then coat the axles with a layer of an all-purpose grease.

■ IF YOU SIMPLY PUSHED your power mower into a corner of the garage last fall after its last mowing session, it's time to be thinking about a spring-cleaning job to ready the machine for the season ahead. Overheating, hard starting, internal engine wear and other serious problems will result if dirt trapped under, on and inside your power mower isn't cleaned away. It takes some effort to have a mower that's ready for use any time: The information on these pages will make that task less troublesome because it covers the nitty-gritty of spring tune-ups.

Start inspection with the blade. A common problem is vibration caused by unbalanced blades. To check balance, remove blade and insert a screwdriver in the mounting hole. Hold the screwdriver vertically; if blade is unbalanced, blade will tip. Using a fine-grit grinding wheel, remove a little metal from the heavy end. If grinding doesn't balance the blade, replace it.

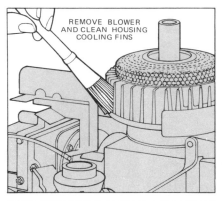

REMOVE BLOWER AND CLEAN HOUSING COOLING FINS

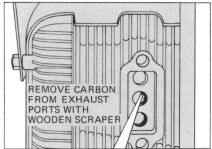

REMOVE CARBON FROM EXHAUST PORTS WITH WOODEN SCRAPER

## EXHAUST PORTS

Carbon is also a form of dirt, and an accumulation of it in the exhaust ports of power-mower engines (two-cycle engines, in particular) will reduce the power output appreciably. Before scraping off the carbon, exercise the precaution of first removing the sparkplug from the engine (to prevent the engine from starting). Then remove the muffler.

Next, turn the crankshaft slowly by means of the starter cord or self-starter until the lower part of the piston covers the ports. In this way, carbon will be kept out of the cylinder when it's scraped loose.

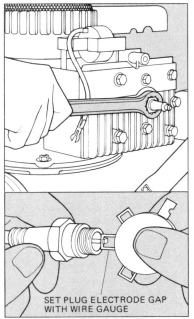

SET PLUG ELECTRODE GAP
WITH WIRE GAUGE

## SPARKPLUG CHECKOUT

Remove the sparkplug and examine it carefully. If the electrodes are burned away or pitted, or if the porcelain is cracked, discard the plug and get a new one of the same designation. You will find the designation printed on the plug. Generally, 100 operating hours should be considered as maximum life for a plug.

If the plug looks fine, use a penknife or small wire brush to scrape dirt from around the electrodes. If you have a compressor, complete the cleaning with a blast of air. Lacking this equipment, blow out particles by mouth.

Whether the plug is new or not, set the electrode gap to the manufacturer's specification with a wire-type, sparkplug gauge like the one shown above. If you've lost the owner's manual and don't know the gap specification, for two-cycle engines gap is set at .028 to .033 in.; for four-cycle, it's .025 to .028. Insert plug and finger-tighten. Then, give an additional half turn with a wrench.

Inspect the sparkplug lead wire. If it is not too badly frayed or damaged, you might be able to patch it with insulating tape. Otherwise, you will have to get at the coil to replace it; in some machines, this means removal of the flywheel—a job best left to a professional. Sometimes, the lead wire is connector-fastened to the coil so that it can be replaced with the coil left in place.

In other mowers, the wire is molded to the coil: To make the change, both wire and coil must be replaced.

## FUEL-OIL MIXTURE

If your power-mower engine is four-cycle, warm it up, then shut it off. Remove the oil drain plug and drain the dirty oil into a waste pan. Replace the drain plug and fill the crankcase through the oil filler to the level mark. Use the type and weight of oil specified in your owner's manual.

In two-cycle engines, a mixture of oil and gasoline is used in the fuel tank. Improper fuel-oil mixture is the main cause of operational problems with two-cycle engines, so check the owner's manual for the correct ratio. (The correct mixture is usually ½ pint to 1 gallon gasoline.) The oil should be of the type and weight specified in the owner's manual or of the type made especially for two-cycle engines.

Insufficient oil in the mixture means that engine parts will be improperly lubricated, resulting in overheating and seizure. Too much oil causes engine smoking, loss of power and sparkplug clogging. So take the time to mix the fuel properly.

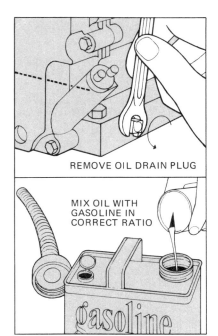

REMOVE OIL DRAIN PLUG

MIX OIL WITH GASOLINE IN CORRECT RATIO

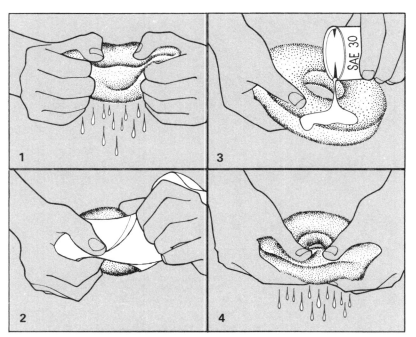

## POLYURETHANE-SPONGE AIR CLEANER

An air cleaner is the primary protection a power mower has from dust particles that can get inside to clog moving parts. One common type of air cleaner has a polyurethane-sponge element as shown in the drawings above. To clean it, (1) wash element in liquid detergent and warm water, (2) wrap in a cloth and squeeze dry, (3) saturate with SAE 30 engine oil and (4) squeeze to remove excess oil. Clean the container that holds the element, replace the element and cover lightly.

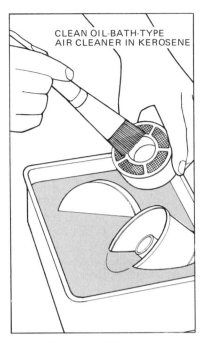

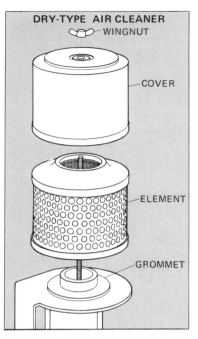

### OIL-BATH CLEANER

This type of air cleaner comes with a container that uses a layer of oil to trap dirt and dust particles.

To clean it, remove air cleaner from the engine and disassemble. Dump out the dirty oil and wash all the parts thoroughly in a solvent such as kerosene. Let these parts air-dry; then reassemble them and fill the cleaner to the level mark with a clean SAE engine oil.

### DRY-TYPE AIR CLEANER

With this type of air cleaner, unscrew the cover as shown above, take out and examine the filter element. If the element is paper, replace it. If it is metallic, carefully tap it on a flat surface to loosen dust and dirt. Then wash it thoroughly. Finally flush the element (from the inside out) with water until the water that comes out of the sides of the element looks clean. Allow the element to dry.

### FUEL-TANK CAP

Some fuel-tank caps have a small vent hole. If it becomes plugged, a vacuum is created that will stop the flow of fuel and the engine will stall. Remove cap and clean out dirt in the hole with a pin. *Take care not to enlarge hole.* In addition, be sure that only proper fuel is poured into the fuel tank (pure gasoline or a correct mixture of oil and gasoline).

### FUEL FILTER

Remove the fuel filter from your power mower and wash it thoroughly in kerosene, or let it soak in engine degreaser. The filter in many small engines is located in the tank-to-fuel-line shutoff valve. Remove the valve to get at the filter (far left).

Other engines have a sediment-bowl-type fuel filter that houses a ceramic element. Remove the bowl. If there is gasoline in the tank, be sure to first turn off the shutoff valve. Disassemble the filter and wash the parts in kerosene. If you're using engine degreaser, soak all parts for an hour or two; then wash in water and dry with an air-pressure hose which also blows away dirt.

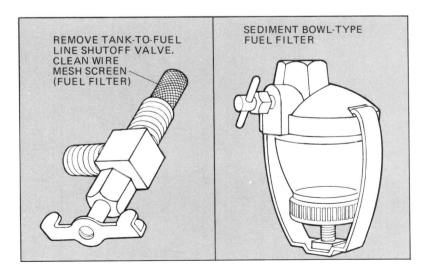

# Hand mowers: Keep your lawn and yourself in shape

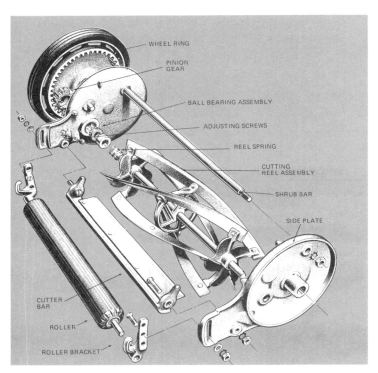

WHEEL RING
PINION GEAR
BALL BEARING ASSEMBLY
ADJUSTING SCREWS
REEL SPRING
CUTTING REEL ASSEMBLY
SHRUB BAR
SIDE PLATE
CUTTER BAR
ROLLER
ROLLER BRACKET

■ PUSHING a hand mower hasn't quite achieved the status of jogging when it comes to exercise. But you *can* work up a nice, warm glow behind a mower and at the same time keep up with your neighbors in exhibiting a neat, trim lawn.

If you have an old manual mower out in the garage or if you run across one at a tag sale, you can get it in working shape fairly easily and at very little expense.

Manual mowers need minimal maintenance. Spend a small amount of your time keeping them in shape, and they'll cut grass every time you want them to go to work.

You can make even a long-neglected reel mower work again by performing the simple maintenance procedures shown here. Basically, you'll need to disassemble it and clean its parts, replace worn or damaged parts, apply lubricant, then prime and paint it. After you've sharpened the blades, your mower will be ready for use.

Pay special attention as you disassemble the mower, so that you can replace the parts in their original positions. If not replaced properly, some parts, such as the right and left pinion gears, will cause problems when you try to put your lawn-mower to use.

### Cleaning mower parts

To get parts thoroughly clean, you may have to apply a rust remover. Wear rubber gloves as you brush the solution onto the rusty surfaces. Then let it soak. Finally, wire-brush parts, rinse with water.

**1** Strip down the mower completely. If necessary, use oil to loosen parts frozen by rust.

**2** Pay particular attention to the reel-shaft bearings. Replace damaged balls or install an entire new bearing if necessary.

**3** If rust is severe, clean parts with solvent to remove grease and oil. Apply a rust remover such as naval jelly. Wear rubber gloves when using remover.

**4** Apply masking tape to parts that won't be painted, including shaft ends, tires, hubs and treads. Peel off excess after carefully cutting with a razor.

**5** Apply oil to the cutting edges of the reel and cutter bar; then spray on red oxide or other primer. Oiled areas won't retain oxide. Wipe them later.

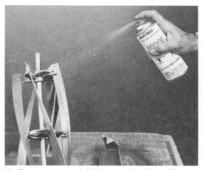

**6** Spray several light coats of quality paint that can be used on metal. We used aluminum on reel and cutter, red on other parts.

**7** Grease gears, bearings and hubs. Carefully replace wheel rings and pinion gears in their proper places or reel will turn in reverse direction.

**8** Stand the mower on end to facilitate replacing the wheels. Jiggle the wheel after it meets the hub to ensure that the gears mesh properly.

**9** Sharpen the cutter bar while it is clamped in a vise. Make flat passes with a smooth, single-cut file on top edge *only*. Stroke with whetstone.

**10** To sharpen reel blades, turn mower upside down, if needed, to adjust cutter bar at ends so it lightly contacts reel blades. Perform steps 11 and 12.

**11** Apply fine-grit grinding compound. This is available at auto-supply stores. This should be applied directly to the inside edge of the cutter bar.

**12** Then rotate the reel *backward* by hand so blades make contact with the bar about a dozen times, lapping up the abrasive along the leading edge.

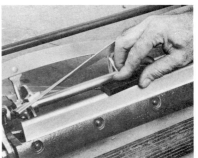

**13** You can give the cutter bar a touch-up sharpening without removing it. Turn the mower over and firmly slide a whetstone across bar's top edge.

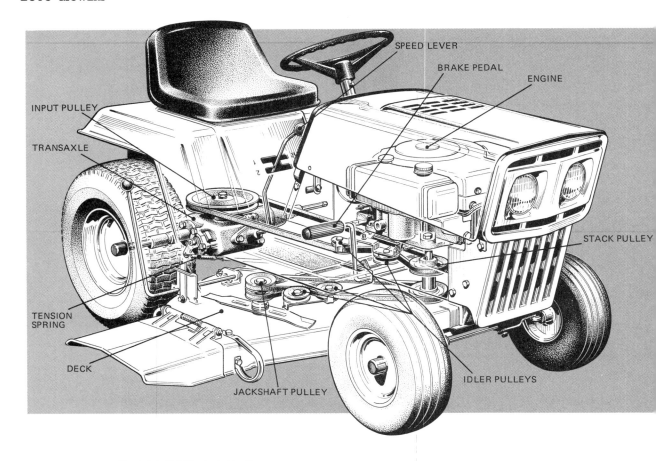

INPUT PULLEY

TRANSAXLE

TENSION SPRING

DECK

JACKSHAFT PULLEY

SPEED LEVER

BRAKE PEDAL

ENGINE

STACK PULLEY

IDLER PULLEYS

# Riding mower selection

■ THIS SPRING many homeowners will be getting ready for a lawn tractor or rear-engine riding mower. Both machines are becoming increasingly popular—especially those in the 8- to 11-hp category.

There are relatively inexpensive lines of mowers that won't stand up to rugged, long-term use. Then there are the better engineered units,

SHOPPING TIPS FOR
SELECTING A MOWER

1 Since all engines need some service, lift the hood and check access to the sparkplug, air filter, oil filter and oil drain. Hood should lock securely.

2 Look at the frame. It should be heavy, welded or bolted steel with a rugged, stamped frame and engine support combined. These frames are sturdy.

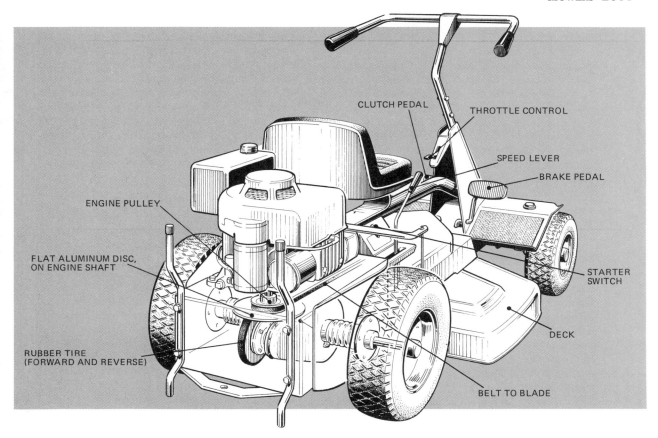

CLUTCH PEDAL
THROTTLE CONTROL
SPEED LEVER
BRAKE PEDAL
ENGINE PULLEY
FLAT ALUMINUM DISC, ON ENGINE SHAFT
STARTER SWITCH
DECK
RUBBER TIRE (FORWARD AND REVERSE)
BELT TO BLADE

built for years of service, that are, naturally, priced higher.

The width of strip a mower can cut (also called swath) ranges from about 30 in. on the 8-hp machines to 42 in. on the 11-hp models. When you make comparisons, remember that a 42-in. mower will cut your yard in half the time needed by a 30-in. unit, providing you maintain a 2-in.

swath overlap. Also, a 36-in. mower will do the job 25 percent faster than one with a 30-in. cut.

Some lawn tractors and rear engine riders have much more precise steering than others. Geared steering, with provision for wear take-up, usually provides less than 1 in. of steering-wheel movement (play) before the front wheels move. This is considered precision steering—with it you can

**3** Sit at the wheel. You should be positioned comfortably with controls convenient. Instruction labeling should be understandable at a glance.

**4** Keyed ignitions give you control of the mower use. When the key is out, the mower shouldn't start. This extra protection is worthwhile.

**5** Seat backs that are as deep as the spread of a hand provide good, basic support and keep you from accidentally sliding off over rough ground.

easily maintain a 2-in. cutting swath overlap.

Units that have more steering-wheel play will probably force you to allow about 3 in. of swath overlap to keep from leaving stray strips of grass. Naturally, more overlap means extra time on the job.

Before buying, determine a mower's turning radius either firsthand or by asking. The tighter the radius, the less hand trimming you'll have to do around trees and plantings. Direct comparisons between two mowers of equal cut width, horsepower and ground speeds have shown that the one with the tightest turning radius saves from 5 to 10 percent of total job time.

### Check the mower blade

The mower blade tip (and shield) should extend beyond the wheels by about 2 in. This is convenient when trimming along flower beds and curbs. The less overhang, the more hand trimming you'll do. Some units accomplish trim overhang by offsetting a narrow mower to the side opposite the discharge chute. Overhang is automatic if the blade tip circle is wider than the tractor wheels.

Authorities say that no more than one-third of the standing height of grass should be removed in one mowing or there can be plant damage. If a spinning blade bounces off the ground, it not only scalps the lawn below proper cutting height, but becomes dull.

Mowers mounted so they tilt with the vehicle's front axle greatly reduce scalping. If the front wheels follow ground contours so will the mower blades.

Scissors hitch-type mountings rely on the rear wheels to adjust the mower's vertical position.

They are more prone to scalping on irregular lawn surfaces, since they are guided by terrain already passed over. Look for antiscalp rollers or wheels mounted on the front of the mower. They also greatly reduce the scalping tendency. The wider the ground-contact surfaces of those rollers, the more accurately they will guide the mower over bumps and slumps. Mowers suspended entirely from the vehicle and without antiscalping rollers, work well only on level lawns.

### Side vs. rear-discharge mowers

Side discharge mowers fan grass clippings over a wider area than do rear discharge machines, which are designed to leave a swath or clipping behind them.

If the rear discharge mowers have a chute between the vehicle's rear wheels, they will leave a relatively narrow swath of clippings and will keep you and the mower cleaner and safer from flying objects. A towed sweeper picks up all debris in one pass. Side discharge mowers with special bagging attachments can do a good job collecting clippings, but the lowest cost and fastest way to remove cuttings is to use a pull-behind sweeper. This lets you dump the clippings from the tractor seat.

### Front vs. rear engine

You'll get a greater feeling of security with a front rather than a rear engine. The front-engine units actually do give greater uphill stability and are better at climbing steep grades. Engine weight placed forward reduces any tendency to tip over backward. As power is applied, leverage action causes a weight transfer which increases rear-wheel traction—especially important when

6 Look for mufflers that direct exhaust away from the driving position and are shielded against possible contact that could cause nasty burns.

7 Front axles must be rugged to take constant pounding. They should be pivoted with a sturdy bolt under the front part of the frame.

8 Geared, automotive-type steering allows more precise guidance than the ''bent rod'' type. Ask to see the steering in model you want.

## TWO GOOD IDEAS IN LAWNMOWER DESIGN

**SIMPLE PIECE** of curved pipe on tractor engines lets you drain oil without the black, greasy stuff drowning other tractor components. Just remove the cap and let the oil run into a container.

**ONE MANUFACTURER** puts a garden-hose fitting on top of its mower decks to aid cleanup. Twist a hose into the fitting, turn on the water and start the mower. The blades wash clippings out.

## TWO DESIGN FEATURES THAT ARE QUESTIONABLE

**SHARP, METAL EDGES** aided by vibration will soon chew through soft insulation around electrical wiring. If the line feeds into such an opening, it should be protected with a soft rubber grommet.

**CABLE** that abrades against rough-punched metal hole edges will fray. This weakens the cable. Also, sharp ends of frayed wire can catch clothing. Better alignment can eliminate this problem.

you use a rear-mounted grass catcher. Vibration is reduced, too, since the engine is physically located farther away from operating position.

Rear-engine units, in turn, give greater forward visibility, are easier to get on and off and usually have less complicated traction-drive belting. You'll be wise to select a machine using belts with the fewest number of turns and twists.

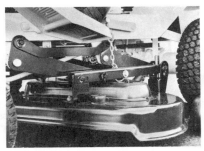

**9** Standard grease fittings make maintenance servicing easier. Check to see that points needing regular lubrication are equipped with nipples.

**10** The mower mount should be of a heavy steel, pivoting on large-diameter pins and giving evidence of careful design, construction and finish.

**11** Finally, ask to look under the mower shroud. Check bearings, welds, blades, finish and baffles. This is the "working" part of your lawnmower.

# Keep your power mower running

■ FAILURE TO START, hard starting and stalling are common mid-season problems that strike gasoline-powered lawnmowers and tractors. The most common causes include lack of compression, lack of or too much fuel in the cylinder, and no spark.

But a major reason for trouble can often be averted by knowing the difference between four and two-cycle engines: In four-cycle engines, ignition occurs with every fourth stroke of the piston. Four-cycle engines burn straight gasoline and possess a separate lubrication (oiling) system. It is imperative that gas and oil *not* be mixed.

In two-cycle engines, ignition occurs every second stroke of the piston. The engine runs on a mixture of oil and gasoline, and failure to mix the correct proportions of gas and oil *properly* is the single greatest cause of trouble (other than sparkplug failure). If yours is a two-cycle engine, consult the owner's manual to determine correct proportions and what kind of gas and oil is recommended. Gas and oil should be thoroughly mixed in a clean container *before* you pour it into the fuel tank.

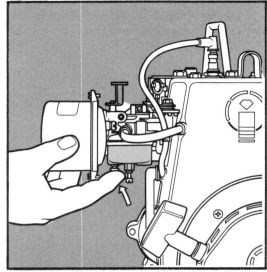

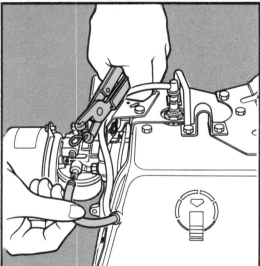

**Engine won't start**

An engine won't start or will stall if fuel isn't getting to the carburetor, and from the carburetor to the cylinder. First, remove the sparkplug and inject two or three squirts of fuel into the cylinder using a clean oil can. Reinsert the plug and crank the engine. If it doesn't start, the cause of the trouble is elsewhere, but if the engine does start, runs for a few seconds and then stops, the problem will be found in the fuel system.

See if there's a drain valve in the base of the carburetor bowl. Press it (top). If no fuel leaks, there's an obstruction in the fuel line or fuel tank. If fuel leaks, there's probably an obstruction in the carburetor. If there is no drain valve, disconnect the fuel line at the bowl (bottom). If no fuel comes out, look for a blocked fuel line or obstruction in the fuel tank. If fuel leaks, a fouled carburetor is probably the cause

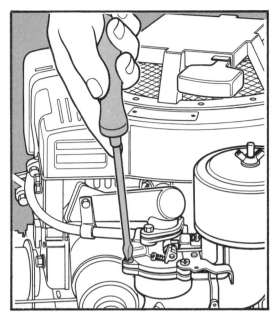

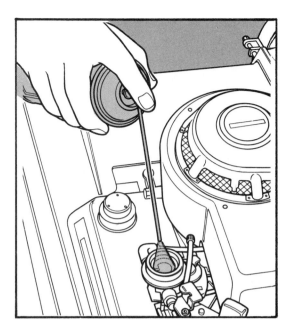

## Blocked fuel line

If the fuel line is blocked, the first step is to check for contaminated fuel. Let some fuel drop into your hand; if water and dirt remain after the gas evaporates, dump all fuel and wash the fuel tank thoroughly with kerosene. It may also be necessary to clean the fuel line and carburetor.

To trouble shoot when fuel isn't getting to the carburetor:

● Replace a bent or clogged fuel line.

● Tighten all carburetor bolts, fuel-line connections and fuel-pump housing (if present) because air leaks destroy the vacuum necessary to pull fuel to the carburetor.

● Clean choke linkage and choke-plate pivots; repair damaged choke parts. Lack of choking action will make the engine hard to start; a choke stuck in the closed

position will flood the engine and prevent starts.

● Clean or replace a dirty fuel filter. One kind is a wire-mesh screen in the fuel line shutoff adapter; other engines have filter bowls.

● Replace the fuel-pump diaphragm if it has any holes.

● Clean clogged screens of fuel pipes that extend from the carburetor into the fuel tank of diaphragm-type carburetors (those without separate fuel pump).

If fuel is not getting from carburetor to engine:

● Clean the air cleaner to reduce flooding.

● Lightly tap the bowl of a float-type carburetor with a screwdriver to loosen a stuck needle valve.

● Adjust the carburetor. Back out the idle-mix screw one turn from finger-tight. Turn the speed screw *in* one turn from where it first touches the throttle lever.

● Last, strip and clean the carburetor thoroughly.

## Inadequate compression

Stated simply, compression is the ability of the piston to compress the fuel/air mixture. Inadequate compression leads to hard starting and loss of power. Poor compression results when a cylinder is scored, piston rings stick or wear, valves stick or wear, or the crankshaft oil seal is damaged. The pressure loss reduces compression, which makes ignition more difficult.

One obvious sign that there is compression loss is a sloppy manual starting cord. If the cord offers little resistance and doesn't snap back, then sufficient compression is questionable.

An accurate check can be made with a compression gauge. Remove the sparkplug, insert the gauge fitting firmly, and crank the engine until the gauge reaches its maximum reading. The *minimum* compression of two-cycle engines is 60 psi; of four-cycles of 4½ hp or less, 65 psi; and of four-cycles above 4½ hp, 70 psi.

Compression loss may be caused by a loose sparkplug. Seat the plug by hand and give it one-half turn with a socket wrench .

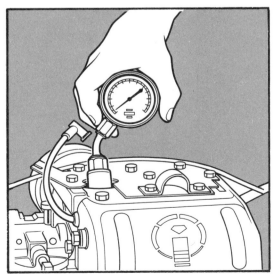

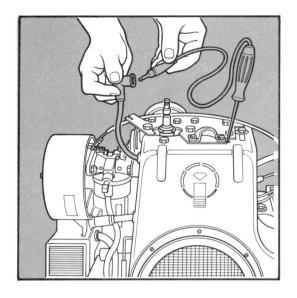

### Garden tractors

Garden tractors with high-horsepower engines usually have transformer-coil ignition systems that are like those in cars, but most powermowers use a magneto system. Magnetos make their own electricity by a magnet-equipped flywheel that revolves around stationary field coils.

You can test a magneto system by gapping either a 14-mm or an 18-mm sparkplug to 5/32-3/16-in. Attach it to the sparkplug lead and ground it against the cylinder head as you crank the engine. A blue spark should jump the electrode gap.

The same test can be made of a transformer-coil ignition system, but use the engine's sparkplug at its normal gap.

Use a spark-intensity tester for checking breakerless systems (left). Disconnect the lead from the sparkplug and attach the tester to the lead's metal terminal. Touch the test instrument's probe to a ground as you crank the engine. The test light will flash if the system is operating properly.

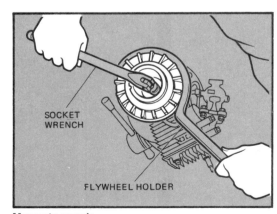

### About sparkplugs

The sparkplug is one of the biggest single causes of engine problems. First, check the owner's manual to make sure you're using the right one. Then make certain the plug lead is connected tightly to the plug terminal, and to the magneto or coil output. If the lead's insulation is cracked, replace the lead. Buy a new sparkplug if the insulator is damaged or if electrodes are worn, burned or heavily coated with carbon or oil. Carbon on a plug usually means an engine is operating on an overly rich fuel mixture or that the ignition output is below par; oil on electrodes usually means that piston rings or valve stems (four-cycle engine) are worn; burned electrodes indicate that the engine is probably overheating.

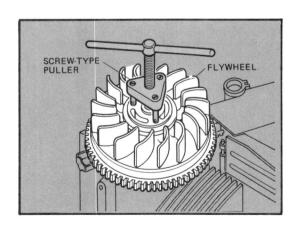

SOCKET WRENCH

FLYWHEEL HOLDER

SCREW-TYPE PULLER

FLYWHEEL

### Magneto repair

To repair a magneto ignition you have to remove the flywheel. On most two-cycle engines, first remove the flywheel nut. Some of these nuts have a right-hand thread; others, left-hand. If the flywheel moves as you turn the nut, hold it fast with a flywheel holder. With the nut off, it can usually be removed. On most four-cycle engines, hold the flywheel with a flywheel holder as the flywheel nut is removed. Install a knockout puller, hold the flywheel firmly, and rap the puller with a hammer to jar the flywheel loose.

**FURNITURE SET** is a two-weekend project. Table and stools are standard and better grade fir. Legs, supports are utility grade.

# Coffee table for your patio

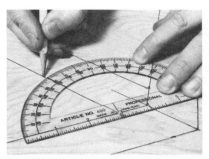

**1. START TABLE** by laying out design on 4 x 4 plywood sheet resting on sawhorses. Use a protractor.

**2A. TRIM OFF** corner of jig at 60° and it can be held firmly against workpiece when cutting with saw.

**4. CUT AND BEVEL** divider strips to fit. One spans the top; other four meet in middle. Predrill for nails.

**2. MAKE A** small accurate marking/cutting jig of plywood and a short 2 x 2 strip to speed layout and cutting.

**3. USING PLYWOOD** pattern, cut and miter six table edges. Predrill nail holes and nail table rim pieces together.

**5. CUT AND FIT** tabletop sections that go between the dividers. Make sure all top pieces are placed best side down.

■ YOU'LL ENJOY your patio or deck far more if you outfit it with this attractive coffee table set.

For appearance, we used a standard or better grade of fir on the table and stool tops. To keep costs down, we used utility grade fir for the table and stool legs and other out-of-sight pieces.

Except for the leg braces (J in the drawing), all angles are 60°. To ensure accuracy, use a sharp point on your pencil to mark all cuts and make certain your saw blade is on the waste side of the line when you cut.

To give you a working surface for both drafting and assembly, lay a 4x4-ft. piece of plywood on a pair of sawhorses. Lay out the tabletop outline on the plywood and draw in the parts that form the top. You then can take the dimensions and angles for the various pieces from the drawing on the plywood panel. To facilitate assembly, do it right on the plywood. Install each piece of wood with its best surface down.

Start by cutting the six table edges (A in the illustration) and beveling their ends. Use your combination square to locate the nail holes for both ends and keep nail locations aligned on all edge pieces. Predrill nail holes with a ⅛-in. drill bit, then line up the edge parts on the plywood

**6. CUT SUPPORT** pieces and test for a tight fit. Run the longest support at right angles to longest divider.

**7. MEASURE SUPPORTS** for at least two screws per section. Drill holes and screw supports to dividers.

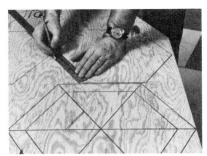

**8. TO LAY OUT** stools, flop plywood panel and draw pattern for stool top on back of plywood panel.

**9. CUT ALL** stool edges to length and bevel. Predrill nail holes before joining edges to form the stool rim.

**10. FASTEN THE STOOL** edges using glue and nails. Repeat the procedure for the remaining stools.

**11. CUT PLYWOOD** seat bottoms and tapered legs, and glue and screw the plywood to legs. Countersink screw heads.

**12. FLOP LEG** assembly and test fit inside stool rim. If plywood fit is not snug, temporarily toenail in place.

**13. WITH STOOL UPRIGHT,** spread glue on plywood and bottom half of edge pieces, and insert stool top pieces.

**14. GLUE IS** probably sufficient, but for strength drill and nail through each stool side into nearest top piece.

pattern and glue them together to form the table rim. When all parts are joined, countersink all nail heads slightly below the surface.

Next, cut the divider strips (B, C and D) to fit. Notice that one strip spans the entire top, running from one point to the point opposite. The other four strips meet in the middle. Bore pilot holes, and nail and glue at the center and through the outside edge points.

Rough-cut the tabletop sections (K, L, M, N, O) that fit between the dividers. Set the outside piece (K) flush against the table edge and leave a 3/16- to ¼-in. gap between the inner pieces. Number sets by the triangular section of the top

| MATERIALS LIST—PATIO TABLE | | |
|---|---|---|
| Key | Pcs. | Size and description (use) |
| A | 6 | 1½ × 2½ × 24″ (table edge) |
| B,C,D | 5 | 1½ × 1½″ × to fit (divider strips) |
| E,F,G | 5 | ¾ × 5½″ × to fit (supports) |
| H | 3 | 1½ × 5½ × 27¾″ (legs) |
| I | 6 | 1½ × 1½ × 5½″ (cleats) |
| J | 3 | 1½ × 1½″ × to fit (leg braces) |
| K | 6 | 1½ × 3½ × 20½″ (top) |
| L | 6 | 1½ × 3½ × 16″ (top) |
| M | 6 | 1½ × 3½ × 12″ (top) |
| N | 6 | 1½ × 3½ × 8″ (top) |
| O | 6 | 1½ × 3½ × 4″ (top) |
| **PATIO STOOLS** | | |
| A | 36 | 1½ × 2½ × 9″ (edges) |
| B | 6 | ½″ plywood cut to fit (seat bottoms) |
| C | 18 | 1½ × 3½ × 14″ (legs) |
| D | 18 | 1½ × 1½″ × to fit (leg braces) |
| E | 36 | 1½ × 3½ × 7½ approx. (top) |
| F | 36 | 1½ × 3½ × 3″ approx. (top) |

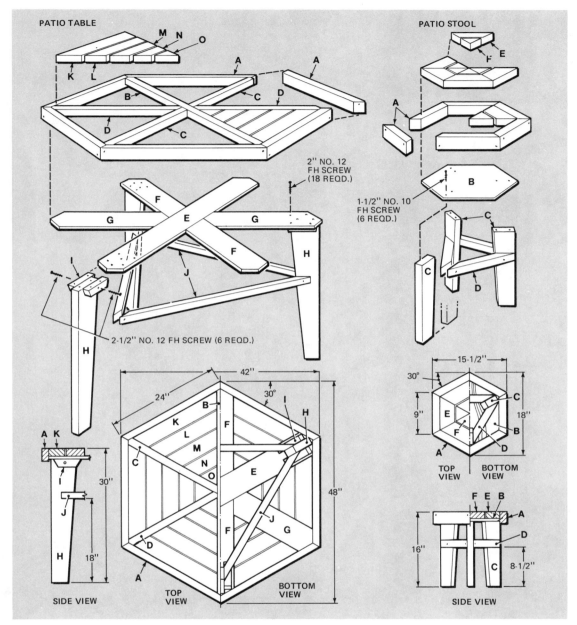

**PATIO TABLE**

**PATIO STOOL**

2" NO. 12
FH SCREW
(18 REQD.)

1-1/2" NO. 10
FH SCREW
(6 REQD.)

2-1/2" NO. 12 FH SCREW (6 REQD.)

42"

24"

30"

48"

18"

SIDE VIEW

TOP VIEW

BOTTOM VIEW

15-1/2"

30°

9°

18"

TOP VIEW

BOTTOM VIEW

16"

8-1/2"

SIDE VIEW

into which they will fit. Mark the tabletop pieces, turn them good side up and miter the ends to fit.

Cut top support pieces (E, F, and G) for a tight fit and position the tapered legs (H) on them. Add the blocks (I). Using at least two screws for each radius section, fasten the supports (E, F and G) to the dividers (B, C and D).

Turn table right side up, spread glue on support pieces and the lower edges of the dividers, and drop all of the mitered tabletop sections (K, L, M, N, O) into place. When top is dry, invert table on sawhorses, trim leg braces (J) to 30°

angles, and position them on the legs 18 in. up from the floor. Nail and glue braces to inside edges of the legs.

Flop the piece of plywood and use the back side to draw a pattern for the stool tops. Cut the parts for all six stools at one time. Lightly label each part with a pencil and make up a separate stack for each stool.

Fill all nail holes and defects with a matching wood putty. Give the table and stools a good sanding with a belt sander, dust and finish with two coats of exterior-grade varnish.

# Classic lawn furniture you can build

■ THE VERY LOOK of this classic wooden lawn furniture conjures up images of more serene times. Though simple in design, this furniture from years past boasts an elegance all its own.

You can use practically any kind of lumber to construct this Adirondack-style furniture. If you apply wood preservative—an undercoat and two top coats of high-quality exterior paint—any species should weather quite well.

We chose a hardwood, poplar, for its added strength.

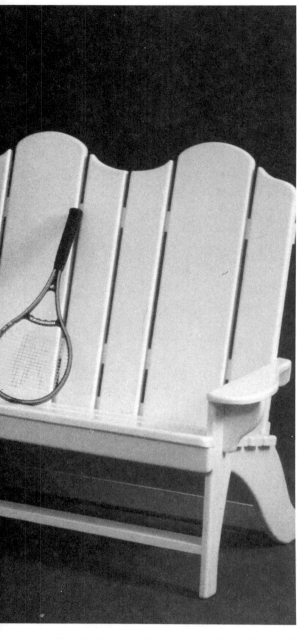

## MATERIALS LIST—SETTEE

| Key | No. | Size and description (use) |
|---|---|---|
| A | 2 | 13/16 × 9 1/4 × 36" poplar (back) |
| B | 2 | 13/16 × 5 × 33 1/2" poplar (back) |
| C | 2 | 13/16 × 5 × 33 1/2" poplar (back) |
| D | 1 | 13/16 × 2 1/2 × 41" poplar (upper cleat) |
| E | 1 | 13/16 × 2 1/2 × 44 1/2" poplar (middle cleat) |
| F | 1 | 13/16 × 2 1/2 × 41" poplar (lower cleat) |
| G | 2 | 13/16 × 5 × 22" poplar (armrest) |
| H | 2 | 13/16 × 4 × 6 1/2" poplar (arm support) |
| I | 2 | 13/16 × 10 × 35" poplar (rear leg) |
| J | 2 | 13/16 × 6 × 22" poplar (front leg) |
| K | 1 | 13/16 × 2 3/4 × 41" poplar (rear stretcher) |
| L | 1 | 1 1/16 × 3 × 44 1/4" poplar (apron) |
| M | 1 | 1 1/16 × 3 × 42 5/8" poplar (front stretcher) |
| N | 2 | 13/16 × 4 × 6" poplar (back support block) |
| O | 1 | 1 1/16 × 3 1/4 × 44 1/4" poplar (seat) |
| P | 2 | 1 1/16 × 3 1/2 × 44 1/4" poplar (seat) |
| Q | 1 | 1 1/16 × 7 × 44 1/4" poplar (seat) |
| R | * | 6d hot-dipped galvanized finishing nails |
| S | * | 4d hot-dipped galvanized nails |
| T | 8 | 2 1/2" No. 10 fh screws |

*As reqd.

## MATERIALS LIST—TABLE

| Key | No. | Size and description (use) |
|---|---|---|
| A | 1 | 13/16 × 9 1/4 × 36 1/4" poplar (top) |
| B | 2 | 13/16 × 5 7/8 × 32" poplar (top) |
| C | 2 | 13/16 × 3 × 26" poplar (apron) |
| D | 2 | 13/16 × 3 × 17 3/8" poplar (apron) |
| E | 4 | 13/16 × 3 × 22" poplar (leg) |
| F | 4 | 13/16 × 2 1/4 × 22" poplar (leg) |
| G | * | 4d hot-dipped galvanized finishing nails |

*As reqd.

## MATERIALS LIST—CHAIR

| Key | No. | Size and description (use) |
|---|---|---|
| A | 1 | 13/16 × 9 1/4 × 36" poplar (back) |
| B | 2 | 13/16 × 5 × 33 1/2" poplar (back) |
| C | 1 | 13/16 × 2 1/2 × 20 1/4" poplar (upper cleat) |
| D | 1 | 13/16 × 2 1/2 × 23 3/4" poplar (middle cleat) |
| E | 1 | 13/16 × 2 1/2 × 20 1/4" poplar (lower cleat) |
| F | 2 | 13/16 × 5 × 22" poplar (armrest) |
| G | 2 | 13/16 × 4 × 6 1/2" poplar (arm support) |
| H | 2 | 13/16 × 10 × 35" poplar (rear leg) |
| I | 2 | 13/16 × 6 × 22" poplar (front leg) |
| J | 1 | 13/16 × 2 3/4 × 20 1/4" poplar (rear stretcher) |
| K | 1 | 13/16 × 3 × 23 1/2" poplar (apron) |
| L | 1 | 13/16 × 3 × 21 7/8" poplar (front stretcher) |
| M | 1 | 13/16 × 3 1/4 × 23 1/2" poplar (seat) |
| N | 2 | 13/16 × 3 1/2 × 23 1/2" poplar (seat) |
| O | 1 | 13/16 × 7 × 23 1/2" poplar (seat) |
| P | * | 4d hot-dipped galvanized nails |
| Q | * | 2" No. 10 fh screws |
| R | * | 6d hot-dipped galvanized finishing nails |
| S | 8 | 2 1/2" No. 10 fh screws |

*As reqd.

The chair and table are made from 4/4 stock (13/16 in. thick), while the settee uses both 4/4 and 5/4 stock (1 1/16 in. thick).

Using the drawing grids for reference, make paper patterns for all contoured parts and trace them onto the appropriate-sized stock. The rear legs should be positioned so that the long part of the leg is in line with the grain direction of the board. When assembled, this will make the leg as strong as possible.

Next, cut the contours with either a band saw or a sabre saw. Then sand out the saw marks from the edge with a drum sander mounted in your drill press or portable drill.

Next, round over all edges except those indicated with an asterisk (*) on the drawing, using a 3/8-in. rounding-over bit in a router. This will give all the pieces a soft, comfortable look, while also reducing the possibility of wood splinters. All edges that have not been removed by the router should be eased with sandpaper before the parts are assembled.

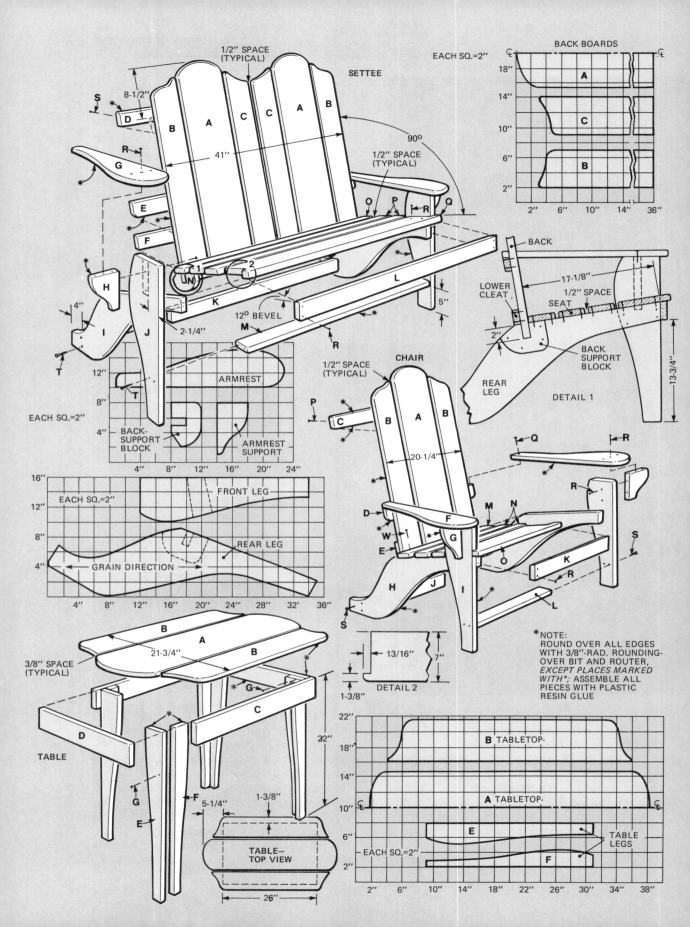

SETTEE

1/2" SPACE (TYPICAL)

8-1/2"

S

D

B   A   C   C   A   B

90°

41"

1/2" SPACE (TYPICAL)

R

G

E

F

H

4"

I   J

2-1/4"

K

12° BEVEL

M

R

O   P   R   Q

L

5"

EACH SQ.=2"

BACK BOARDS

18"
14"
10"
6"
2"

A

C

B

2"   6"   10"   14"   36"

BACK

LOWER CLEAT

17-1/8"

1/2" SPACE

SEAT

2"

BACK SUPPORT BLOCK

REAR LEG

13-3/4"

DETAIL 1

12"

ARMREST

8"

T

1/2" SPACE (TYPICAL)

CHAIR

4"   BACK-SUPPORT BLOCK

ARMREST SUPPORT

EACH SQ.=2"

4"   8"   12"   16"   20"   24"

16"

FRONT LEG

12"

EACH SQ.=2"

8"

REAR LEG

4"

GRAIN DIRECTION

4"   8"   12"   16"   20"   24"   28"   32"   36"

P

C

B   A   B

20-1/4"

D

F

W

E

M   N

G

O

R

Q

R

S

K

R

S

H   J   I

L

13/16"   7"

DETAIL 2

1-3/8"

*NOTE:
ROUND OVER ALL EDGES
WITH 3/8"-RAD. ROUNDING-
OVER BIT AND ROUTER,
*EXCEPT PLACES MARKED
WITH*;* ASSEMBLE ALL
PIECES WITH PLASTIC
RESIN GLUE

B   A   B

21-3/4"

3/8" SPACE (TYPICAL)

G

C

D

TABLE

G

F

E

22"

5-1/4"   1-3/8"

TABLE—TOP VIEW

26"

22"
18"
14"
10"
6"
2"

B TABLETOP-

A TABLETOP-

E

EACH SQ.=2"

F

TABLE LEGS

2"   6"   10"   14"   18"   22"   26"   30"   34"   38"

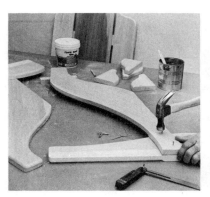

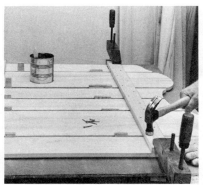

**1 START EACH** assembly with legs. Use plastic resin glue throughout.

**2 CLAMP CLEATS** to back boards, then nail. Use spacers for accuracy.

**3 BAR CLAMP** at back and spacing strip on front keep legs aligned.

Use highly water-resistant plastic resin glue for all assemblies. It is far less expensive than waterproof resorcinol glue and will serve quite well for this application. Also, hot-dipped galvanized nails are used throughout.

Because hardwood is being used, the nailing will be more difficult—a difficulty compounded by using the generally rough and nubby hot-dipped galvanized nails. For this reason, you may want to drill pilot holes for the nails.

In any case, do not nail closer than ¼ in. to the edge of the board and ⅜ in. to the end of a board without using a pilot hole.

Assemble the chair and settee in the following order: Glue and nail the back support blocks to the rear legs, then attach the rear legs to the front legs. Join the armrest support to the front legs, then assemble the backs as separate units. Use ½-in.-thick spacers to keep the back boards aligned properly.

Apply glue, then clamp and nail the cleats to the back boards, as shown in the photo.

Keep in mind that the middle cleat is 3¾ in. longer than the backboard assembly is wide to accommodate the armrests. Just center it on the back. When the armrests are finally attached, the cleat ends can be cut to exactly the size and shape needed for a professional-looking fit.

Next, support the leg assembly in the upright position as shown in photo No. 3, and slide the back assembly into the notched supports. Then attach the aprons, stretchers and armrests and you are finished.

Assemble the table by first joining the aprons, then nailing the top boards in place. Nail the leg parts together. Then glue and nail the completed legs to the aprons from the inside.

To complete the job, sand all surfaces thoroughly and apply a high-quality wood preservative following the manufacturer's directions on the can. Then give all the pieces three coats of paint.

# Harvest table you can build with your chain saw

■ ALTHOUGH THE rough-hewn features of this handsome table and bench set give an impression of stability and agelessness, you can actually build it in a weekend work session, if you organize your work schedule. The sturdy furniture will withstand years of use and weather in your backyard and retain the same timeless appeal that it has today.

Cutting the large wood members that give the furniture its rugged look is made easier with a heavy-duty chain saw.

**WHEN CROSSCUTTING** a heavy overhang, make two cuts from opposite sides to prevent splitting.

**YOU CAN BREAK** out the waste slices by hand. If some pieces are stubborn, use a chisel or pinch bar.

**MAKE A SHORT** crosscut at the end; then make an angle cut to avoid splitting the wood.

**MAKE FOUR** or five kerf cuts to notch out the post top. Use a wood strip as a depth guide.

**IN ORDER TO LEVEL** the bottom safely, you can easily make use of the chain saw itself.

**LINE UP** the 2x4s with their best surfaces on the top. Identify each piece in order of assembly.

**IF YOU MUST** bore the holes with a portable drill, a drill guide like this is invaluable.

**HOLD SAW** at a 45° angle to trim off excess. Keep your body to the left of the chain line.

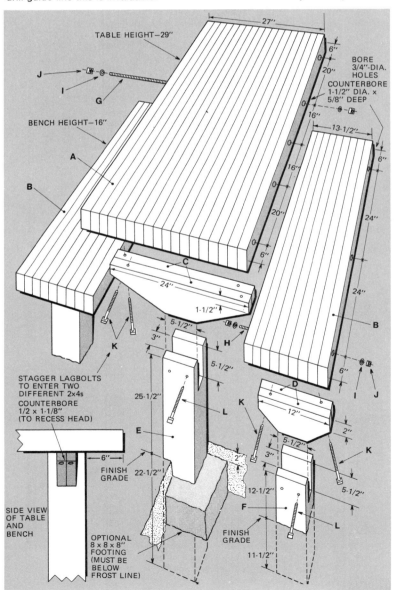

TABLE HEIGHT—29"

27"

6"

20"

BORE 3/4"-DIA. HOLES COUNTERBORE 1-1/2" DIA. x 5/8" DEEP

J

I

G

BENCH HEIGHT—16"

16"

13-1/2"

A

B

16"

20"

24"

24"

6"

C

24"

B

1-1/2"

5-1/2"

3"

H

K

5-1/2"

D

STAGGER LAGBOLTS TO ENTER TWO DIFFERENT 2x4s COUNTERBORE 1/2 x 1-1/8" (TO RECESS HEAD)

25-1/2"

L

K

12"

2"

E

5-1/2"

K

6"

FINISH GRADE

22-1/2"

2"

3"

SIDE VIEW OF TABLE AND BENCH

12-1/2"

F

L

OPTIONAL 8 x 8 x 8" FOOTING (MUST BE BELOW FROST LINE)

FINISH GRADE

11-1/2"

**USE A BELT** sander on edges. Assemble top carefully so it won't need sanding. Use same procedure for seats.

### MATERIALS LIST—TABLE, BENCHES

| Key | No. | Size and description (use) |
|-----|-----|----------------------------|
| A | 18 | 2×4" × 7' Wolmanized lumber (tabletop pieces) |
| B | 18 | 2×4" × 5' Wolmanized lumber (benchtop pieces) |
| C | 4 | 2×6×24" Wolmanized lumber (tabletop supports) |
| D | 8 | 2×6×12" Wolmanized lumber (benchtop supports) |
| E | 2 | 6×6×48" Wolmanized lumber (table legs) |
| F | 4 | 6×6×24" Wolmanized lumber (bench legs) |
| G | 5 | 1/2"-dia. × 27" threaded rod (tabletop rods) |
| H | 6 | 1/2"-dia. × 13 1/2" threaded rod (benchtop rods) |
| I | 22 | 1/2"-i.d. washers |
| J | 22 | 1/2"-i.d. nuts |
| K | 16 | 3/8"-dia. × 6" lagscrews (top fasteners) |
| L | 12 | 3/8"-dia. × 5" lagscrews (leg fasteners) |

Legs on the benches and table are of 6x6 Wolmanized lumber notched at the top to receive doubled 2x6 supports for the top and seats. Both the table and benchtops are 2x4s laid on edge and bolted together with a threaded rod.

Begin work by cutting the posts (E and F, see drawing and materials list). Post stock is usually available in 6-, 8- and 12-ft. lengths. *Be sure to wear safety goggles at all times while you're working with the chain saw.*

To avoid tearing the ends of the wood when crosscutting, first make a partial cut from one edge of the wood. Then turn the stock over and complete the cut by sawing through from the opposite side.

The tops of the posts are notched to accommodate the supports for the furniture tops. Before you make the notches, set the posts in the ground. However, the posts must be placed accurately or you will have alignment problems later. You may find it easier to construct and assemble the units out of the ground, and then plant them.

Begin work on the notches by cutting a series of saw kerfs. To make these cuts the post must be rigid. So, if it is not in the ground, first clamp the post to a sturdy support such as a sawbuck. Mark the outline of the notch and tack-nail a strip of wood across the post to serve as a visual guide for the depth of the cut. Start the cut with the chain bar pointing slightly upward. Level the bar off as the cut progresses; continue until you reach the guide stick.

After you've made several side-by-side kerf cuts, you may be tempted to tilt the saw sideways to nibble away at the bottoms of the waste slices. *Don't do it*—you could easily lose control of the saw and experience a kickback, as the teeth at the top of the bar strike wood and cut in the opposite direction. It's much safer to break away the waste slices by hand or with a chisel. Then you can use the saw to level off the remaining stubs at the notch bottom.

### Cutting the top supports

Next, cut the angled supports (C) for the tabletop, and the supports (D) for the benchtops. Clamp a 2x6 support board to a pair of sawhorses and make a partial crosscut to establish the end. Then make the angled cut to meet it. In this way, the piece will make a clean break from the waste without splitting. Nail two supports together and smooth the edges with a belt sander. As an alternative, you can join the two pieces of 2x6 together first, and then make the cuts in one pass.

Insert the supports into the posts, clamp them if necessary, and bore the holes for the lag bolts. Put these aside.

### Making the furniture tops

Align the 2x4s (A and B) for the table and benchtops on their edges. Select the best surfaces for the face sides. Arrange the 2x4s so that any slightly warped ones are positioned in alternate directions to counteract each other. Severely warped or twisted stock should not be used.

Mark the pieces so the tops can be reassembled later, in the same order. Use a T-square to mark the locations for the threaded rod holes.

If you have a drill press, clamp a stop to the table to simplify centering across the width. Otherwise, use a drill guide to bore all holes perpendicular. First, counterbore the holes on the two outside members to recess the nuts and washers. Bore the larger hole first, otherwise the drill center will be lost.

Cut the ½-in.-dia. threaded rod to length and grind off the burrs. Assemble the pieces and clamp strips of wood across the top and bottom at both ends and in the center to obtain a good surface alignment. Insert the threaded rods and washers. Then secure the nuts at both ends, using a pair of socket wrenches.

If you use stock size 2x4 lumber, you'll have to trim off the waste at one end. You can easily do this with the chain saw. However, the resulting edge will be rough and will need smoothing with a belt sander and 80-grit paper.

### Assembling the pieces

You can use the same procedure to assemble both the table and the benches. Begin by turning one of the tops face down on the ground. Bore holes for the lag screws through the supports and into the top. Assemble and place the unit into the holes that have been dug for it. Repeat for the other furniture pieces.

Back-fill and tamp the earth firmly. You can top off the holes with 6 or 8 in. of cement for extra stability if you wish. For added permanency, consider pouring concrete collars around the posts.

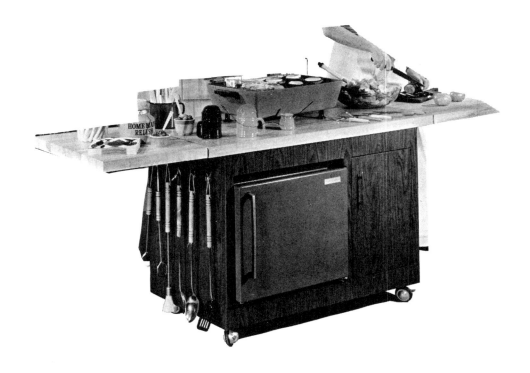

# Mobile cook-center

■ THIS COOK-CENTER has a lot going for it if you enjoy year-round entertaining. During the warm months it's sure to draw raves from your neighbors and guests when they spot it on your patio. At season's end, you simply roll it indoors for use in the family room. And when it's not in service, it's a handsome piece of furniture that will suit any room decor.

### The cart's parts

The concept started with the electric barbecue cooker. The cooker shown can be used outside (indoors in a fireplace) for barbecues and, with its lid closed, for delicate Chinese smoke cooking.

The other piece of equipment that played a major part in the cart's design is the miniature refrigerator.

The plastic-laminated countertop is an exciting product, too. The butcher block pattern looks like the real thing. The drop leaves, on which you cut and prepare vegetables, are the real thing, made up of laminated strips of maple.

### Building the cart

To build your cart, it's a must to have your mini-refrigerator on hand. It will determine the final size of the cart (except for height). The top on the cart shown is at a comfortable, and recommended, cooking height when used with the electric barbecue. If possible, do not alter this dimension.

Start building by laying out the cart parts on two sheets of plywood. Before cutting, take time to double-check those critical dimensions concerning the refrigerator. Assemble the cabinet using waterproof glue, then apply the plastic laminate using contact cement. You can flop the box over so you can trim the laminate overhang using your router and a carbide cutter, but you will have to do some hand filing to square the four corners in each of the two openings at the front.

Next, make the cabinet top. After cutting the two pieces, use waterproof glue and 1¼-in. No. 8 screws to join the pieces. The top can now be covered with plastic laminate. Do the edges first and finish by applying the top.

Glue up the maple chopping blocks (or consider having this step done at your local lumber yard mill) and fasten these to the countertop using 2-in. brass-plated continuous hinge. Make absolutely certain that you drill adequate-size pilot holes in the maple chopping blocks for the hinge screws or you are almost sure to pop the heads off a number of screws.

Although the weight of the top itself holds it in place, you'd be well advised to anchor it using one lagscrew as shown in the drawing. The four

corner blocks prevent lateral movement of the top, but at any social gathering there is a chance that a guest will lean on one of the upraised drop leaves. With the cooker going full blast, that could cause a tragedy. The single anchor absolutely prevents any chance of tilting the top.

When you're satisfied with the installation, remove the lagscrew and top so you will have less weight to handle while you work on remaining details. For example, the cart can now be rested on its back and the casters attached. This makes it easier to move the cart around as you advance to the finishing stages. Right the cabinet and you can go to work installing the flush-mounted storage door (after first fitting and laminating it). Pick a pair of flush-mount hinges that will match the door pull.

The barbecue tools hang from 2-in. brass L-hooks. Simply lay out your set of tools as you prefer and turn the hooks into predrilled pilot

## Exploded view of the mobile cook-center

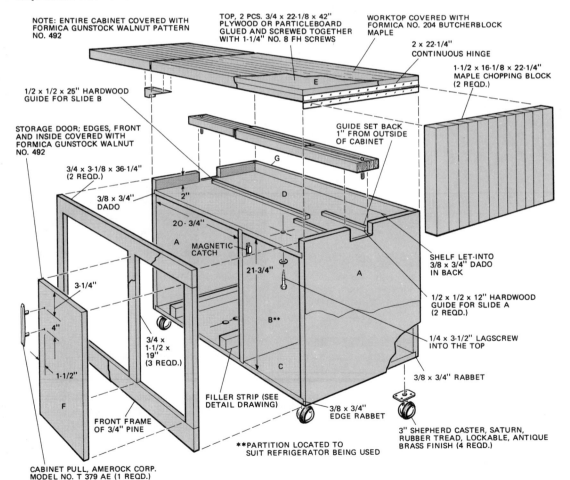

NOTE: ENTIRE CABINET COVERED WITH FORMICA GUNSTOCK WALNUT PATTERN NO. 492

TOP, 2 PCS. 3/4 x 22-1/8 x 42" PLYWOOD OR PARTICLEBOARD GLUED AND SCREWED TOGETHER WITH 1-1/4" NO. 8 FH SCREWS

WORKTOP COVERED WITH FORMICA NO. 204 BUTCHERBLOCK MAPLE

2 x 22-1/4" CONTINUOUS HINGE

1-1/2 x 16-1/8 x 22-1/4" MAPLE CHOPPING BLOCK (2 REQD.)

1/2 x 1/2 x 25" HARDWOOD GUIDE FOR SLIDE B

STORAGE DOOR; EDGES, FRONT AND INSIDE COVERED WITH FORMICA GUNSTOCK WALNUT NO. 492

GUIDE SET BACK 1" FROM OUTSIDE OF CABINET

3/4 x 3-1/8 x 36-1/4" (2 REQD.)

3/8 x 3/4" DADO

2"

20-3/4"

MAGNETIC CATCH

21-3/4"

SHELF LET-INTO 3/8 x 3/4" DADO IN BACK

1/2 x 1/2 x 12" HARDWOOD GUIDE FOR SLIDE A (2 REQD.)

3-1/4"

4"

1-1/2"

3/4 x 1-1/2 x 19" (3 REQD.)

B**

1/4 x 3-1/2" LAGSCREW INTO THE TOP

3/8 x 3/4" RABBET

FILLER STRIP (SEE DETAIL DRAWING)

3/8 x 3/4" EDGE RABBET

FRONT FRAME OF 3/4" PINE

3" SHEPHERD CASTER, SATURN, RUBBER TREAD, LOCKABLE, ANTIQUE BRASS FINISH (4 REQD.)

**PARTITION LOCATED TO SUIT REFRIGERATOR BEING USED

CABINET PULL, AMEROCK CORP. MODEL NO. T 379 AE (1 REQD.)

### HOW TO MAKE THE SLIDE SUPPORTS

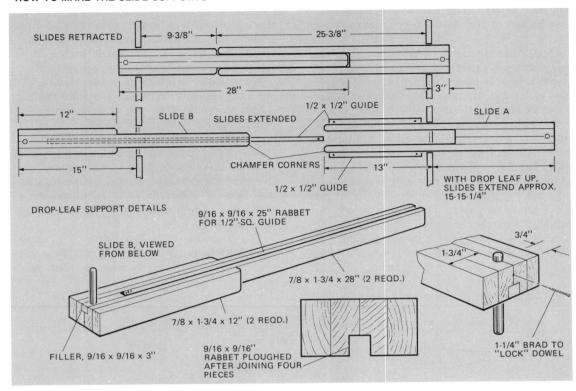

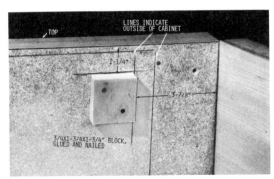

**TO LOCATE TOP** on its base, place the top on unit and measure overhang on all four sides. Then, using a pencil, draw the cabinet outline on the top. Flip top and locate one block at each corner.

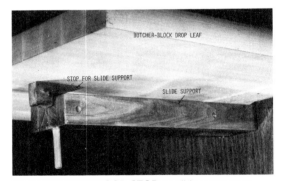

**POSITION HARDWOOD STOP** so slide support assures drop leaf is level with cabinet top when extended.

holes. If your cooking-tool collection is substantial, add hooks at the right end of the cabinet.

The side supports for holding up the drop leaves look trickier to build than they actually are. Take the time to study the details in the drawings and photos. Notice that slide **B** insets into slide **A** when both are pushed into the cabinet. You'll need four lengths of hardwood 28 in. long and four lengths 12 in. long to make the pair. After gluing up the supports, plough the

rabbet along the length of slide **B**, which will travel on the ½-in. square guide. You can cut a blind rabbet, but it is easier to run the full length of the slide and then add a small filler strip at the outboard end.

After making your slides, position them in the cabinet to mark the guide location. This is a good time to check the stop position when slides are retracted. They should stop with 3 in. projecting from the cabinet.

**REFRIGERATOR COMPARTMENT** must be sized to suit model. Size shims so refrigerator slides in and out easily, with space at top for air circulation.

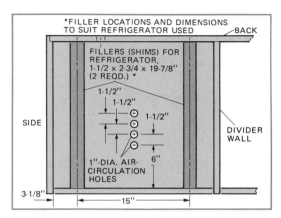

**ADEQUATE VENTING** is a must. Drill minimum of four holes—more if you select larger refrigerator. Then glue and tack shims beneath.

To locate the small triangle-shaped slide support stops, lift the first drop leaf and extend the support exactly 15 in. *Note:* The slide should butt the stop snugly so the leaf is level with the top. When you get this position, mark and drill for fastening the stop. Repeat the procedure on the second drop leaf.

The final step is to install the shims (fillers) on which the refrigerator rests. They should be level with, or slightly higher than, the bottom rail so the refrigerator can be easily removed.

**BARBECUE TOOLS** are always ready on this cart. Hooks are spaced to suit your tool collection. More tools can be hung on the other side of the cabinet.

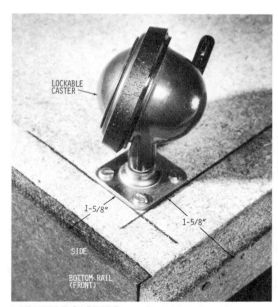

**LOCKABLE CASTERS** permit cart to roll easily on patio surface. The casters used here are mobility-rated at 100 lbs each.

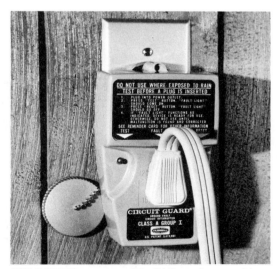

**FOR SAFETY,** use ground fault interrupter on outdoor outlet. Use No. 12-ga. extension cord to power refrigerator and cooker.

# **P**ark-bench furniture for your patio

**FURNITURE** is built of oak and strip of mild steel. Countersunk nuts and bolts join parts.

■ STARTING with the familiar-looking park bench, we've created an original patio furniture set that home craftsmen can duplicate. For a look of sheer elegance, we used oak for the wooden slats; the metal portions of the pieces are fashioned of ³⁄₁₆ by 1½-in. hot-rolled mild steel—a metal that you *can* work with.

The set consists of a bench, two chairs, a dining-sized table and a plant stand. The furniture is comfortable to use, easy to make and relatively inexpensive—in short, a nice project for a weekend workshopper to tackle.

If you have never worked with and bent metal before, you needn't be concerned. The fabrication procedures we have worked out have been especially tailored to meet the needs of a beginning metalworker. All the bending is done with simple, homemade jigs. Plans for making the jigs and information on using them are given on the following pages.

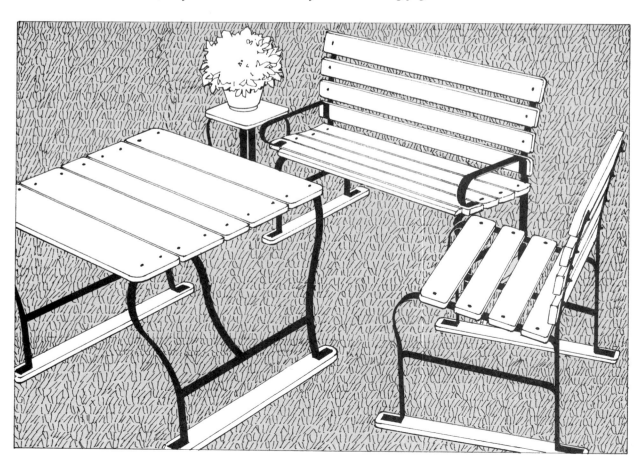

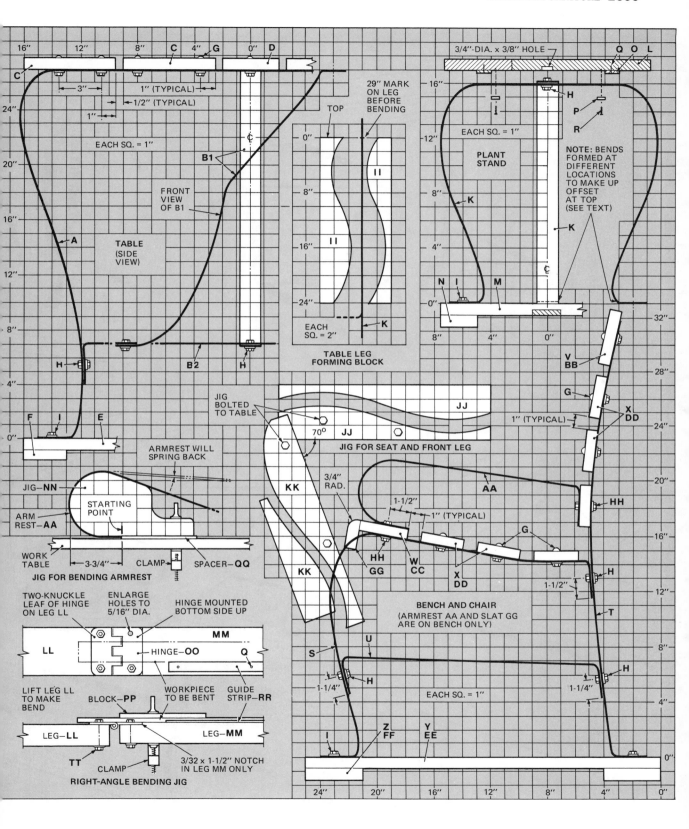

TABLE (SIDE VIEW)

FRONT VIEW OF B1

EACH SQ. = 1"

TABLE LEG FORMING BLOCK

29" MARK ON LEG BEFORE BENDING

TOP

EACH SQ. = 2"

3/4"-DIA. x 3/8" HOLE

PLANT STAND

EACH SQ. = 1"

NOTE: BENDS FORMED AT DIFFERENT LOCATIONS TO MAKE UP OFFSET AT TOP (SEE TEXT)

JIG BOLTED TO TABLE

70°

JIG FOR SEAT AND FRONT LEG

3/4" RAD.

1-1/2"

1" (TYPICAL)

1" (TYPICAL)

BENCH AND CHAIR (ARMREST AA AND SLAT GG ARE ON BENCH ONLY)

1-1/2"

1-1/4"

1-1/4"

EACH SQ. = 1"

ARMREST WILL SPRING BACK

JIG—NN

STARTING POINT

ARM REST—AA

WORK TABLE

3-3/4"

CLAMP

SPACER—QQ

JIG FOR BENDING ARMREST

TWO-KNUCKLE LEAF OF HINGE ON LEG LL

ENLARGE HOLES TO 5/16" DIA.

HINGE MOUNTED BOTTOM SIDE UP

HINGE—OO

LIFT LEG LL TO MAKE BEND

WORKPIECE TO BE BENT

GUIDE STRIP—RR

BLOCK—PP

LEG—LL

LEG—MM

3/32 x 1-1/2" NOTCH IN LEG MM ONLY

CLAMP

RIGHT-ANGLE BENDING JIG

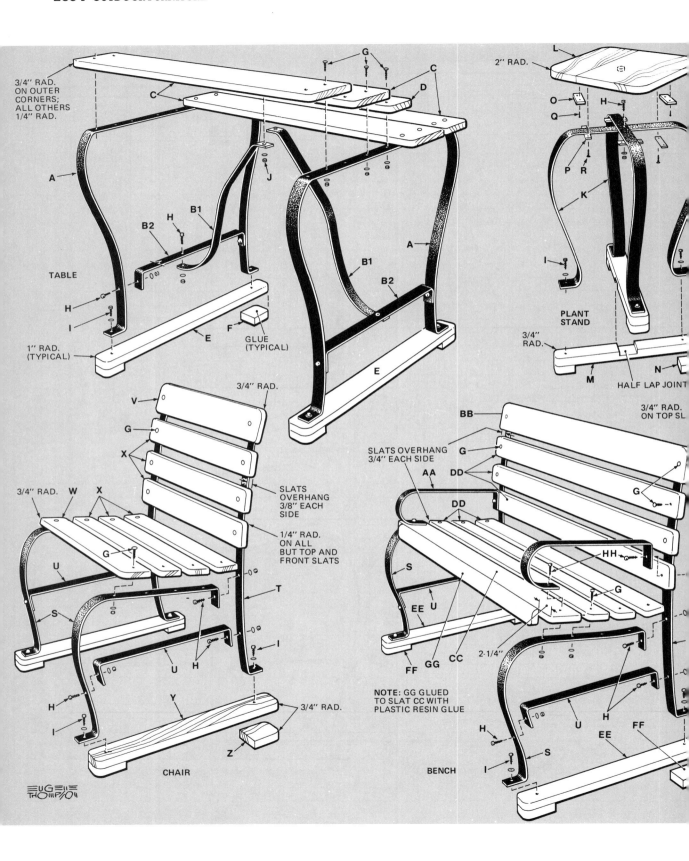

3/4" RAD. ON OUTER CORNERS; ALL OTHERS 1/4" RAD.

G

C

C

D

2" RAD.

L

O

H

Q

P  R

K

A

I

B1

B2  H

J

PLANT STAND

TABLE

H

A

B1

I

B2

1" RAD. (TYPICAL)

E

F

GLUE (TYPICAL)

E

3/4" RAD.

HALF LAP JOINT

M

N

3/4" RAD.

V

G

3/4" RAD. ON TOP SL

X

BB

G

SLATS OVERHANG 3/8" EACH SIDE

SLATS OVERHANG 3/4" EACH SIDE

G

3/4" RAD.  W

X

AA

DD

1/4" RAD. ON ALL BUT TOP AND FRONT SLATS

DD

G

U

G

HH

S

T

S

EE  U

G

U  H

I

F

G

H

Y

CC

GG

2-1/4"

Z

H

3/4" RAD.

NOTE: GG GLUED TO SLAT CC WITH PLASTIC RESIN GLUE

FF

CHAIR

H

U  H

BENCH

EE  FF

I

S

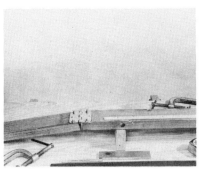

**1** To make small-radius bender, attach hinge, upside down, between 2x4s. Two-knuckle leaf goes on short 2x4.

**2** Clamp strip to be bent between the hinge and a steel hold-down block. Use a wood guide strip.

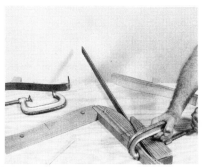

**3** Squeeze mating curved blocks together to make leg's front contour. Small bend at end is formed before this.

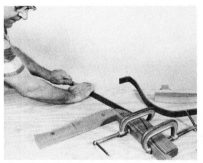

**4** The strip is further bent around the corner by hand. Keep strip's edge flat against worktable.

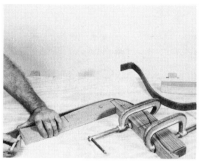

**5** Hold strip against former blocks, then mark block end. Temporarily remove strip and transfer to other jig.

**6** Next, make the small radius bend. This view shows why seat contour must not be bent before this operation.

The oak slats are $^{13}/_{16}$ in. thick—just as the wood comes from the lumberyard. You can buy the metal at a local iron-supply house, welding shop or from an ornamental iron worker. When you buy the metal strips, make certain you specify *mild steel* because anything that is tougher won't bend readily in the jigs we have designed.

### Where to start

Begin by making the three bending jigs shown. The curved sections can be cut with either jig, band or sabre saw. If, during the cutting, any irregular bumps are cut on the edge, make certain you smooth them out using a rasp and sandpaper—or you will transfer the bumps to the metal.

### Use a strong hinge

The long right-angle bender is made with a door hinge mounted back-side up between two lengths of 2x4 stock. It is *very important* that you select a strong hinge. While developing the prototype jig, we discovered that the quality of several unknown-brand hinges was poor: They fractured behind the knuckles when subjected to the force that was required to make the bends in the steel.

Rebore the two outer holes in each leaf to permit insertion of $^5/_{16}$-in. bolts. Attach the two-knuckle leaf to the shorter length of 2x4, as indicated in the drawing.

### The bench

Cut a strip of steel 38 in. long to form the

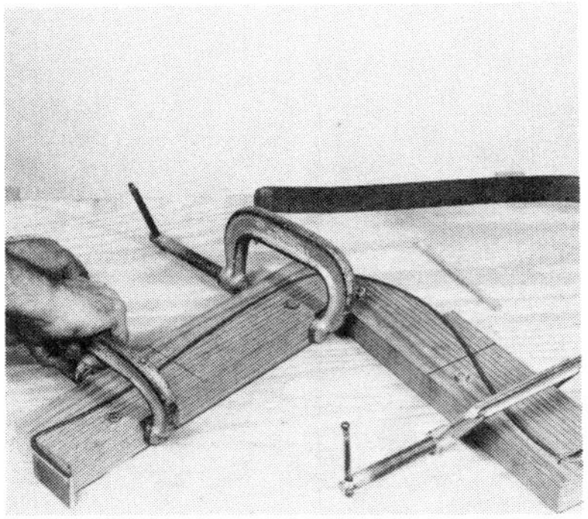

**7** Return strip to contour jig, then apply pressure by squeezing clamps to complete forming strip.

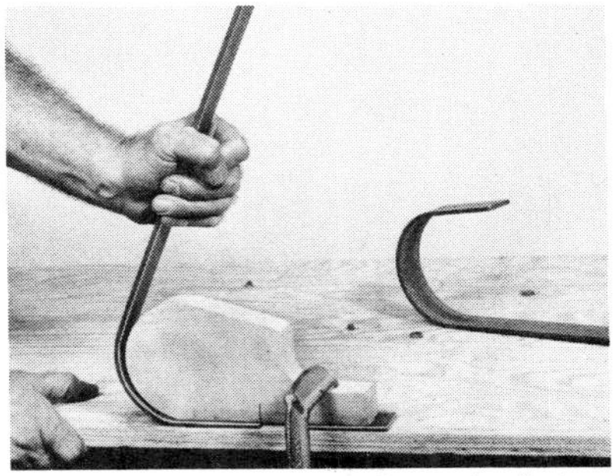

**8** Clamp armrest-former jig vertically to worktable. Use a bar clamp over high spot to prevent block from lifting. Remove clamp after bend is started. Grasp the strip low.

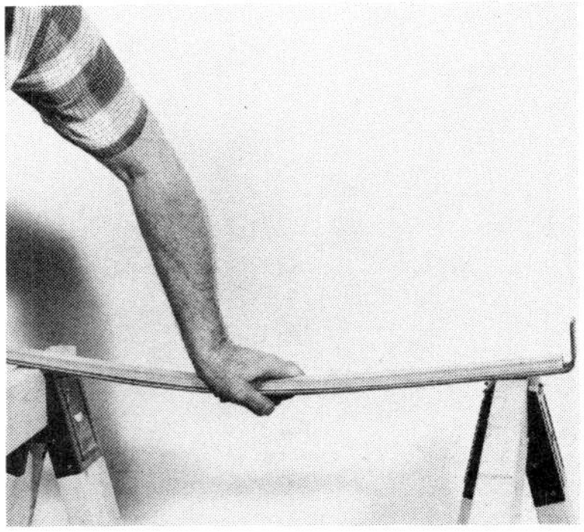

**9** Use a strip of plywood and two sawhorses to fashion the large-radius, gentle curve for the rear legs.

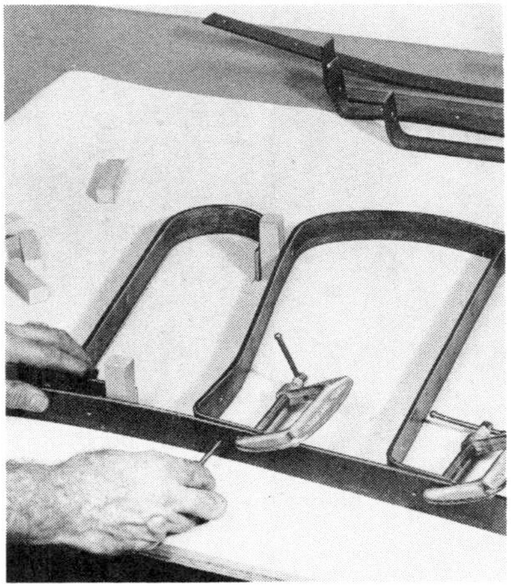

**10** Drill holes in uprights, then clamp all pieces together to mark hole locations in abutting pieces.

| Key | No. | Size and description (use) |
|---|---|---|
| | | **TABLE** |
| A | 2 | 3/16 x 1½ x 90″ steel (leg) |
| B | 4 | 3/16 x 1½ x 28″ steel (brace) |
| C | 4 | 13/16 x 6½ x 36″ oak (slat) |
| D | 1 | 13/16 x 4 x 36″ oak (middle slat) |
| E | 2 | 13/16 x 3 x 32″ oak (base) |
| F | 4 | 13/16 x 3 x 3″ oak (base foot) |
| G | 18 | ¼ x 1″ carriage bolt, nut and lockwasher |
| H | 6 | ¼ x 1″ machine bolt, nut and lockwasher |
| I | 4 | ¼ x 1½″ lagscrew and lockwasher |
| J | 2 | ¼ x ⅞″ lagscrew and lockwasher |
| | | **PLANT STAND** |
| K | 2 | 3/16 x 1½ x 48″ steel (leg) |
| L | 1 | 13/16 x 11½ x 11½″ oak (top) |
| M | 2 | 13/16 x 2 x 15″ oak (base) |
| N | 4 | 13/16 x 2 x 2½″ oak (base foot) |
| O | 2 | 3/16 x 1 x 3″ wood shim |
| P | 4 | ½ x 3″ mending plate |
| Q | 4 | ½″ brads |
| R | 8 | 1″ No. 8 fh screws |
| H | 1 | ¼ x 1″ machine bolt, nut and lockwasher |
| I | 4 | ¼ x 1½″ lagscrew and lockwasher |
| | | **CHAIR** |
| S | 2 | 3/16 x 1½ x 38″ steel (leg) |
| T | 2 | 3/16 x 1½ x 34″ steel (back support and leg) |
| U | 2 | 3/16 x 1½ x 23″ steel (brace) |
| V | 1 | 13/16 x 4 x 18″ oak (top slat) |
| W | 1 | 13/16 x 3½ x 18″ oak (front slat) |
| X | 6 | 13/16 x 3 x 18″ oak (slat) |
| Y | 2 | 13/16 x 2 x 24″ oak (base) |
| Z | 4 | 13/16 x 2 x 3″ oak (base foot) |
| G | 16 | ¼ x 1¼″ carriage bolt, nut and lockwasher |
| H | 6 | ¼ x 1″ machine bolt, nut and lockwasher |
| I | 4 | ¼ x 1½″ lagscrew and lockwasher |
| | | **BENCH** |
| S | 2 | 3/16 x 1½ x 38″ steel (leg) |
| T | 2 | 3/16 x 1½ x 34″ steel (back support and leg) |
| AA | 2 | 3/16 x 1½ x 25″ steel (arm rest) |
| U | 2 | 3/16 x 1½ x 23″ steel (leg brace) |
| BB | 1 | 13/16 x 4 x 43″ oak (top slat) |
| CC | 1 | 13/16 x 3½ x 43″ oak (front slat) |
| DD | 6 | 13/16 x 3 x 43″ oak (slats) |
| EE | 2 | 13/16 x 3 x 25″ oak (base) |
| FF | 4 | 13/16 x 3 x 4″ oak (base foot) |
| GG | 1 | 13/16 x 2 x 38½″ oak (skirt) |
| G | 12 | ¼ x 1¼″ carriage bolt, nut and lockwasher |
| HH | 4 | ¼ x 1½″ machine bolt, nut and lockwasher |
| H | 6 | ¼ x 1″ machine bolt, nut and lockwasher |
| I | 4 | ¼ x 1½″ lagscrew and lockwasher |
| | | **JIGS** |
| II | 1 | 1½ x 5½ x 24″ fir (cut as shown) |
| JJ | 1 | 1½ x 3½ x 15″ fir (cut as shown) |
| KK | 1 | 1½ x 3½ x 16″ fir (cut as shown) |
| LL | 1 | 1½ x 3½ x 24″ fir |
| MM | 1 | 1½ x 3½ x 38″ fir |
| NN | 1 | 13/16 x 5 x 9″ oak (cut as shown) |
| OO | 1 | 3½ x 3½″ wrought steel hinge Stanley No. 758 (or Stanley No. 741) |
| PP | 1 | ⅜ x 1½ x 6″ steel |
| QQ | 1 | 3/16 x 1½ x 6″ steel |
| RR | 1 | ⅛ x ¾ x 20″ fir |
| SS | 4 | 1″ No. 8. fh screws |
| TT | 4 | 5/16 x 2″ machine bolt, nut washer |

front-leg/seat section. Make a grease-pencil mark 2¼ in. from one end. Place the mark over the center of the hinge. Clamp the strip to the long 2x4 together with a piece of ⅜x1½x5-in. steel (or use two pieces of scrap 3/16-in. working stock). Place this hold-down block ½ in. from the bend mark. Clamp firmly, close to the hinge, then lift the jig's short leg to form the bend.

Next, bolt the two sections of the leg/seat formers to a scrap board. Place the strip against the lower section, position the mating block, then squeeze with clamps. With the clamps in place, bend the strip around the corner by hand. Do *not* form the seat curve yet. Instead, make a mark for the small radius bend at the end of the former-block. Remove the strip from the jig and place it in the hinged bender. Locate the mark 1 in. from the center of the hinge (toward the long 2x4) and make the bend. Return the strip to the curved jig, and use clamps to form the seat curve. Centerlines marked on the jig pieces will aid alignment. Note that the fixed sections of the jig are positioned at an exaggerated angle to each other. This allows for spring-back.

To make the lower brace, use a strip 23 in. long. Mark bending lines 2½ in. from each end.

Center the mark over the hinge knuckles, clamp and make the bend.

The back upright is bent freehand because a jig of appropriate size would waste quite a bit of lumber. Use a 34-in. length of stock. Make the small-radius bend first, then place a strip of ½x2-in. plywood over the metal and put it over two sawhorses.

You should apply downward hand pressure at the center to obtain an even curve. Check the bend against the drawing.

The armrest is made with a 25-in. strip. Before forming the large curve, make a bend mark 3 in. from the other end.

Then clamp the armrest forming-block vertically to the work table over a piece of scrap strip. Slide the end of the work strip into the gap as shown in the drawing.

Use a bar clamp over the high point of the jig to hold it down during the initial phase of the bending. Bend the strip upward by hand, then remove the bar clamp and continue the bend. Transfer the piece to the right-angle jig and make the small-radius bend.

Mark the uprights for hole locations, then center punch and drill ¼-in.-dia. holes. Clamp the lower brace and armrest in place to accurately mark aligning hole centers. Scraps of wood the same thickness as the slats should be used as spacers when clamping the armrest in place.

Cut the wood stock to length, then rip to the necessary widths. Highly water-resistant plastic resin glue is used to join the 2-in. strip to the front slat and to make the base feet.

Apply metal primer and two coats of satin finish paint to the metal before final assembly. Spray paint cans will do the job; they are tough and quick drying. Also paint the bolts and screws for attaching the wood before final assembly.

To obtain a lasting clear finish to the wood, apply three coats of a quality weatherproof top-coat.

### Planter

The legs for the planter are formed using the same jigs as for the bench, except the second part of the forming jig is not used. Since the legs cross over each other at the top, one set of legs is made slightly longer to make up the offset. This is accomplished by making the small-radius bends for the feet of differing dimensions.

Make a mark 1½ in. in from each end on one strip and 1¾ in. from the ends on the other. Place these marks over the knuckle of the hinge and make the bends.

Position and clamp the strip in the curve-forming jig so the corner of the small radius is 1 in. from the bottom end of the jig.

You should take up on the clamp to form the curve, then make the upper bend by hand while the strip is still clamped in place. Drill a hole for a ¼x1-in. bolt through the top center of both pieces. Also drill holes for ¼x1½-in. lagscrews in the feet.

Cut the top from a piece of 11½-in.-wide oak stock. Bore a blind ¾-in. hole ⅜ in. deep in the bottom center to allow clearance for the bolt head. The legs are secured to the top by bridging 3-in. mending plates over each leg section. Use two ³⁄₁₆-in.-thick wood strips, nailed in place, to shim the gaps resulting from the overlap. The base is made with two pieces of stock as shown.

### Table

A different forming jig is required for the table legs. Make it by cutting an "S" curve through a 24-in. piece of 2x6 lumber as shown.

Cut two pieces of strip 90 in. long, then make marks at 2¼ in. and at 29 in. in from each end.

You form the bends for the feet by setting the 2¼-in. mark over the hinge knuckle. Next, place the strip between the formers so the 29-in. mark lines up with the top edge of the blocks. Use two clamps to form the curve. With the clamps still engaged, make the upper bend by hand.

Four 28-in. lengths of steel are required for the table braces. To make the lower horizontals, make bending marks 2¼ in. from each end; place the strip with the mark over the hinge knuckle and make the bend.

The curved braces are made using the chair-leg jig and a vise. Start by making the right angle bends 2¼ in. from the end. Then place the small bent end of the piece in a vise and make a slight return bend by hand. Form the sweeping curve in the chair-leg jig, using only the larger section. Clamp the flat end of the strip against the convex portion of the block and make the bend by hand.

Bore the holes for the bolts and screws as indicated in the drawing, then cut the wood to size.

The next step is to connect the braces; now lay out the tabletop slats on the work table, bottom side up and spaced ½ in. apart. Place the metal frame onto the slats and mark the center holes for the carriage bolts.

### Chair

The chairs are made in the same manner as the bench, but with the armrests excluded. Also, the stiffener strip under the front slat is not required.

# Aluminum-and-canvas chairs

■ THESE aluminum-and-canvas chairs can help you get ready for summer entertaining and relaxing. You can make them from ¾-in. do-it-yourself aluminum tubing with 90° elbow and T-butt connectors, available at hardware and building supply dealers.

Tools you need are minimal: steel tape measure, masking tape, large square, drill, hammer, screwdriver, hacksaw or tubing cutter, parallel clamp, center punch and Pop riveter.

**Cutting:** A hacksaw or tubing cutter can be used to cut the tubing. The cutter makes a more accurate cut, but the tubing will need reaming afterward. The saw cut needs less reaming but must be filed smooth.

**Joining:** Besides using 90° elbow and T-butt connectors, ¾-in. tubes can be joined together by fitting a piece of ⅞-in. tube over them and securing it in place with Pop rivets.

**Bending:** You can make 5-in.-radius bends in the tubing with a simple jig. When making bends be sure to carefully line up the dimension marks on your tube with the index mark on the jig to insure properly fitting parts. Also clamp the tubing between the jig blocks to prevent it from sliding during bending. Pull slowly so the tubing won't buckle. To help apply pressure when you make the bends, brace yourself against the table.

# FOOTSTOOL

The jig for bending the tubing is a 10-in.-dia. wood disc of ¾-in. stock (with index marks drawn through the center) and two pairs of support blocks. Each pair consists of a ¾ x 1¾ x 13-in. block and a ¾ x 1¾ x 17-in. block, with a ¾-in. space between them for the tubing. A successful project depends on your bending the tubing accurately. For best visibility, it helps to make the bend dimension marks on masking tape pressed on the tubing. If you lay the jig parallel to the table edge, you can easily check right-angle bends with a large square.

**Step 1:** On a 6-ft. length of tubing, mark off 24 in. from each end. Place one tube end in the support blocks, carefully match the tube mark nearest that end with an index mark on the disc, clamp and make a 90° bend. Pull slowly and apply pressure. Repeat on the other end to form a U.

**Step 2:** Make a mark at 13 in. from each tube end. Place the tube ends into the jig so that the upright part is vertical as shown while you make the third and fourth bends. Make a 90° sideways bend at both ends. Afterward mark off 10½ in. from the ends, which will be cut off.

**Step 3:** Tubing can be cut accurately with a tubing cutter. The cutter curls the ends inward, so they must be reamed before the joints can be fitted. You might prefer using a hacksaw, then smoothing the ends after cutting.

**Step 4:** Repeat preceding steps to make a second unit. Then join sections with two 5-in. x ⅞-in.-dia. pieces of aluminum tubing telescoped over the ¾-in. tubing ends. Drill two holes through one side of the tubing; secure with Pop rivets.

The covering is made from a 17½ x 37½-in. piece of canvas. Join the short ends with a ¾-in. seam. Sew a 1-in. hem with a ¾-in. turn-under on the sides.

THIS EDGE
OF SHORT BLOCK
TANGENT TO DISC

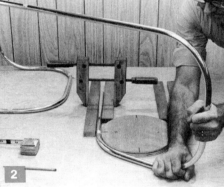

**MATERIALS**
6′ x ¾″-dia. tubes (2)
5″ x ⅞″-dia. tubes (2)
Pop rivets (4)
17½ x 37½″ canvas (1)

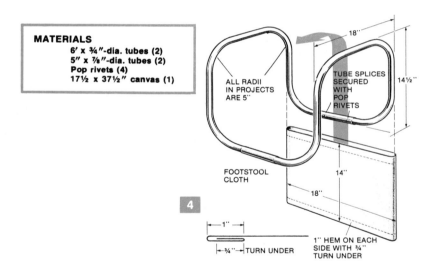

ALL RADII
IN PROJECTS
ARE 5″

18″

TUBE SPLICES
SECURED
WITH
POP
RIVETS

14½″

FOOTSTOOL
CLOTH

14″

18″

1″

¾″ TURN UNDER

1″ HEM ON EACH
SIDE WITH ¾″
TURN UNDER

# SMALL CHAIR

**Step 1:** To make the small chair, it's best to begin by making the chair back. Start with a 6-ft. length of ¾-in. tube and carefully mark off 23¾ in. from each end. Place a tube end in the bending block, match the tube mark nearest that end with the index mark on the jig and bend the tube 90°. Repeat with the other tube end to form a U.

Then give the back a slight backward bend for comfort. You can do this by marking off 17½ in. at both ends. Place the tube ends in the jig on edge and bend each side about 2½ in. off the axis.

To make the chair sides, begin with a 6-ft. length of ¾-in. tubing. Mark one end at 15⅜ in. and the other at 34¼ in. Placing each end in the blocks, match the

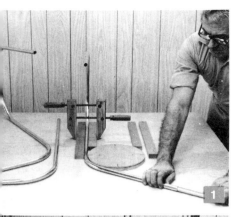

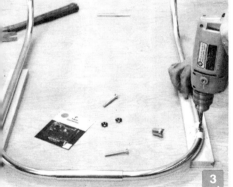

index marks with the tube marks nearest the end in the blocks and make 90° bends at both marks.

Now make a mark at 19¼ in. from the longer end and place the "U" part of the tube in the jig on edge. Grip the tube end to make a sideways bend which will be the third bend. To provide leverage to bend the short tube end, inset a ⅝-in. dowel into the tube as shown. This short length is the base of the chair.

Repeat the process for the second side, but make the third (base) bend in the opposite direction so the two sides (left and right) will join.

**Step 2:** Make a mark at 7⅜ in. from the base end of each side and cut off that excess. Join the two sections with a ⅞ x 5-in. tube splice secured with two Pop rivets.

**Step 3:** T-butt connectors (8) are used to assemble the parts. Allow an extra ⅛ in. for them when you're cutting the two cross tubes on the chair front and marking the base for the holes. For example, spacing between the chair sides is 17½ in., but the cross tubes are cut 17¼ in. to allow for the two connectors. The top cross brace is 13¼-in. high and the bottom cross brace is 2-in. high. The T-butt connectors consist of a locknut, connector and ¼-20 oval-head bolt.

To install the cross tubes, use a punch to get an accurate start, then drill a ¼-in. hole in the outside tube as shown. Use the oval-head bolt that comes with the connector to dimple (recess) the hole for

a neat appearance. Lay the tub on a 2 x 4-in. board that has a ⅜-in. hole drilled in it to accommodate the bolt. Insert the bolt and strike its head with a hammer to make a neat dimple.

**Step 4:** After the bolt is inserted through the hole, place the connector over it and attach the locknut. Insert the tube as shown and tighten the bolt. The locknut spreads out against the tube wall when the bolt is tigthened.

**Step 5:** After you attach the sides to the two front cross tubes, insert the back into the base and then into the horizontal ends. The T-butt connectors can be removed, then reinserted. Later, the back will be loosened to insert the seat cloth.

**Step 6:** Cut the back cloth to the dimensions given. Finish the curved area with bias tape and fold the cloth in half. Make a ¾-in. side seam and a 1-in. bottom hem with a ¾-in. turn-under.

**Step 7:** Cut a 23½-in. canvas square for the seat. Make 1-in. front and back hems with ¾-in. turn-unders. Then sew 1½-in. side hems with ¾-in. turn-unders.

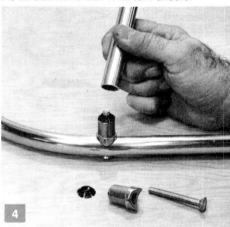

**MATERIALS**

6' x ¾"-dia. tubes (3)
3' x ¾"-dia. tube (1)
¾" T-butt connectors (8)
5" x ⅞"-dia. tube (1)
20½ x 31½" canvas
23½ x 23½" canvas

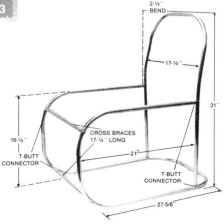

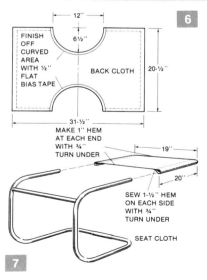

# LARGE CHAIR

**Step 1:** To make the two sides, begin with an 8-ft. length of ¾-in. tube. Make marks at 8¾-in. and 39¼-in. from each end. Place the tube ends in the block and make the 8¾-in. bends at right angles on both ends. (Since only a small piece of tube will be held in the block, join a scrap piece of tube to the short end with a dowel and clamp firmly.) Next place the long middle part of the tube in the blocks and make the 39¼-in. bends to close the rectangle as shown. Join ends with a 5-in. x ⅞-in.-dia. tube splice and two Pop rivets, then make the second side.

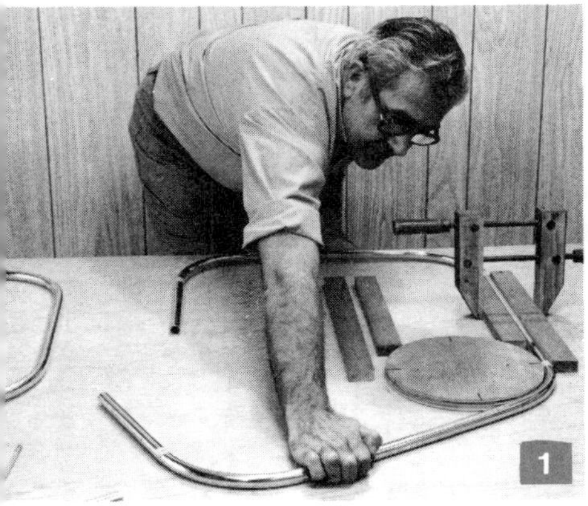

**Step 2:** To make the back, begin with a 48-in. length of tube (8 ft. halved) and mark one end at 44 in. Again add a temporary piece of scrap tubing with a ⅝-in. dowel as shown in the drawing so a sufficient amount of the tube can be held in the jig blocks. Bend two pieces in this way to 90° angles, then cut off ½ in. at their shorter, rounded ends.

**Step 3:** Still working with the two back pieces of tube, mark off 13 in. from their straight ends. Place the straight end of the tubing in the jig so the short bent end is held vertically in the air and makes a 104° angle. This will be the angle between the back and seat. You can mark the angle on the worktable as a guide. Bend one piece to the left, one to the right.

**Step 4:** You can make the upper back joint by inserting a piece of ⅝-in. hardwood dowel between the two tube ends. Two small nails will prevent the dowel from shifting and keep the joint secure. (A ⅞-in. tube splice as used before would make a bump in the canvas cover.)

**Step 5:** The front cross tube that is part of the seat is attached with a pair of 90° elbow fittings. Cut the cross tube to 17¼-in. length. (Elbow fittings have a 1⅛-in. makeup to complete the 19½-in. crossbar dimension.) Twist the fittings on either end of the tube clockwise to tightly secure them. Insert the free end of the elbows without the locknuts in the open end of the seat tube as shown.

**Step 6:** The elbow ends in the seat tubes are secured with a self-tapping setscrew driven into the casting, as shown in the photo, when canvas is in place. Next cut three pieces of 19¼-in.

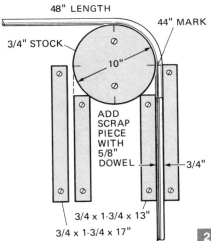

48" LENGTH

44" MARK

3/4" STOCK

10"

ADD SCRAP PIECE WITH 5/8" DOWEL

3/4"

3/4 x 1-3/4 x 13"

3/4 x 1-3/4 x 17"

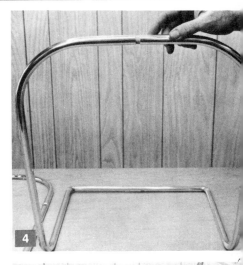

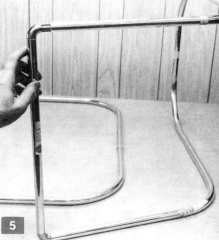

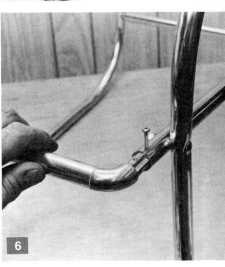

**MATERIALS**
8' x ¾"-dia. tubes (4)
5" x ⅞"-dia. tubes (2)
T-butt connectors (6)
90° elbow connectors (2)
1⅝" x ¼-20 oval-head bolts with nuts (2)
5" x ⅝"-dia. dowel (1)
Pop rivets (4)
⅝" setscrews (2)
23½ x 58¼" canvas (1)

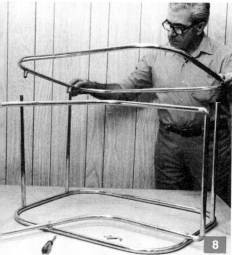

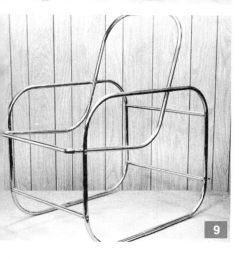

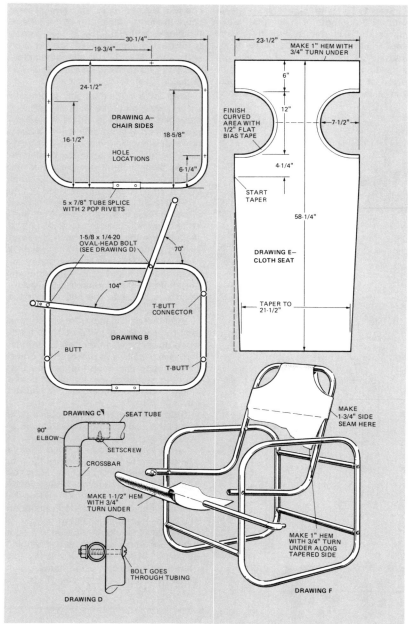

DRAWING A—
CHAIR SIDES

HOLE
LOCATIONS

30-1/4"
19-3/4"
24-1/2"
16-1/2"
18-5/8"
6-1/4"

5 x 7/8" TUBE SPLICE
WITH 2 POP RIVETS

1-5/8 x 1/4-20
OVAL-HEAD BOLT
(SEE DRAWING D)
70°

104°

T-BUTT
CONNECTOR

DRAWING B

BUTT

T-BUTT

DRAWING C
90°
ELBOW

SEAT TUBE

SETSCREW

CROSSBAR

MAKE 1-1/2" HEM
WITH 3/4"
TURN UNDER

BOLT GOES
THROUGH TUBING

DRAWING D

23-1/2"
MAKE 1" HEM WITH
3/4" TURN UNDER
6"
12"
7-1/2"
FINISH
CURVED
AREA WITH
1/2" FLAT
BIAS TAPE
4-1/4"
START
TAPER
58-1/4"
DRAWING E—
CLOTH SEAT
TAPER TO
21-1/2"

MAKE
1-3/4" SIDE
SEAM HERE

MAKE 1" HEM
WITH 3/4" TURN
UNDER ALONG
TAPERED SIDE

DRAWING F

tube for the lower front crossbar and two back crossbars.

**Step 7:** Now you can drill the sides to receive the assembly bolts. Locate holes as shown in drawing A. Dimple the holes and insert the T-butt connectors and bolts as indicated in drawing B. Clamps and masking tape make an otherwise difficult job easy. Parts can be held together with tape to check alignment.

**Step 8:** Assembly should be done by first attaching the seat to one side, installing the three cross tubes with T-butt connectors, attaching the seat section with bolts as in drawing D, then adding the other side. All bolts should be tightened firmly after assembly.

**Step 9:** To make the cover, cut the canvas as shown and finish the curved area with bias tape, then taper the sides. Make a 1-in. top hem with a ¾-in. turn-under, then fold the top part over. Sew a 1¾-in. side seam as shown in drawing F. Make a 1-in. side hem with a ¾-in. turn-under along the tapered sides. Finally, sew a 1½-in. bottom hem with a ¾-in. turn-under. Then slip the canvas over the back; slide seat bar through bottom hem.

# Stowaway tables for the outdoors

THE TABLE ABOVE can be opened on one or both sides for serving and closes to only 7 inches wide. Table below breaks down into four separate parts for easy storage

■ IMAGINE HAVING a Christmas display on your lawn 12 months of the year simply because it is too big and bulky to put away! You can liken this to a bulky picnic table that sits around from one summer to the next, too large to stow away come winter, a headache to move each time you must mow around it. And before long, its ap-

pearance starts disintegrating from constant exposure to the elements.

Not so with the two unique tables shown on these pages. You can take them apart, close them up, move them indoors if you wish, or park them in the garage in a minimum space.

The 3×6-ft. table in the photograph breaks down into four parts—two benchtops, stretcher and a table that folds flat. To set it up, you place the table face down and open the wood turn-buttons which hold the legs in tow and the metal ones which anchor the leg braces. Lift one leg, back off the wingnuts, swing open the twin bench legs and insert the stretcher part way in its slot. Then lift the opposite leg, swing out the bench legs, raise both side braces, shove the notched stretcher in place and pull up on it to lock it. Turn the table right side up, open the notched rails on the underside of the benchtops and fit them into the notches in the legs. This procedure may sound complicated, but once your family gets used to it you will be surprised how quickly the table will be ready for your picnic.

### Two sheets of plywood

It takes two 4×8-ft. sheets of plywood (with some waste) for the legs, table and benchtops, and 1×2, 1×3, 1×4 and 2×4 lumber for the rest. You'll need 20 3-in. plain butt hinges, four wingnuts and bolts, six metal turnbuttons and about six dozen 1¼-in. No. 8 flathead screws, along with some water-resistant glue. A couple coats of a marine-type spar varnish inside and out give good protection for the plywood table and benchtops. Two coats of acrylic latex house paint will keep the legs in good condition and will add some color to the table.

You'll need a saber saw to cut the legs, but it's worth the small extra charge to have the lumberyard saw your plywood into the nine individual pieces required. This way, there won't be much cutting to be done and a handsaw will handle what's left. Kerfing of the table and benchtops adds to the looks, but is optional. The kerfs are easy to cut if you have a router or portable circular saw.

It's important that the leg hinges at the top fit flush in their rabbets so the side braces will pass over the barrels when moved up or down. Note too that the end-view drawing shows a ¾-in.-sq. block added to the tops of the bench legs to bear against the underside of the benchtops for added support.

### The second table

The fold-down table is light enough to carry to a deck or yard and elegant enough to use inside, too. It doesn't look like a plywood table (even though the panels are) because the edges are banded with ¾-in. solid stock. You can use any hardwood from mahogany (which we used to get

**THE FOUR PARTS** of this collapsible table are the stretcher (A), benchtops (B), and table (C). The bench and the table legs hinge to the tabletop. Use the cutting diagrams (right) to minimize waste

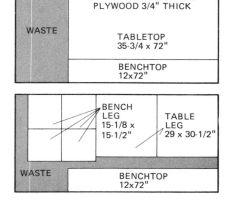

CUTTING DIAGRAMS

4x8' EXTERIOR-GRADE PLYWOOD 3/4" THICK

WASTE

TABLETOP
35-3/4 x 72"

BENCHTOP
12x72"

BENCH LEG
15-1/8 x 15-1/2"

TABLE LEG
29 x 30-1/2"

WASTE

BENCHTOP
12x72"

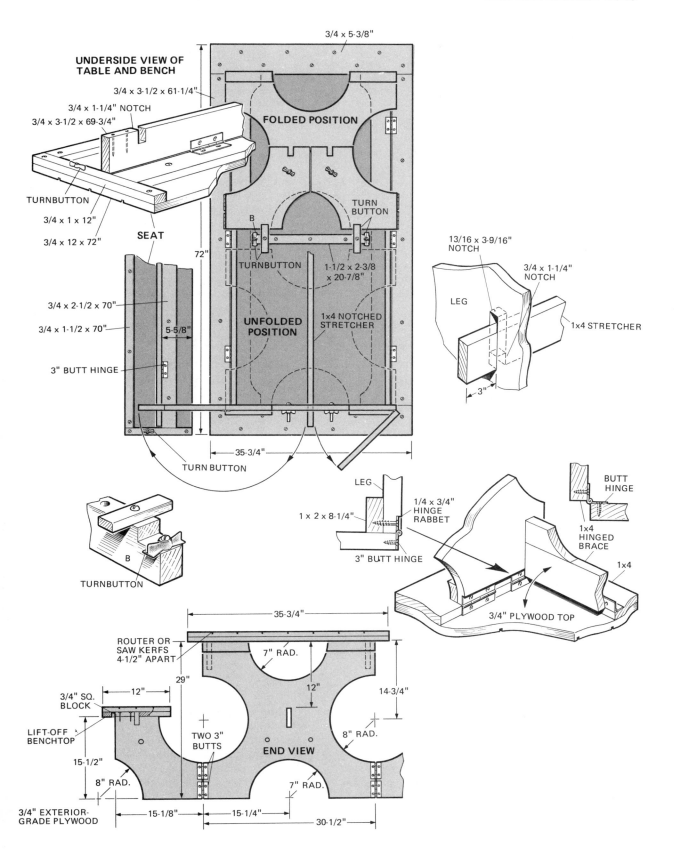

**UNDERSIDE VIEW OF TABLE AND BENCH**

3/4 x 3-1/2 x 61-1/4"

3/4 x 1-1/4" NOTCH

3/4 x 3-1/2 x 69-3/4"

TURNBUTTON

3/4 x 1 x 12"

3/4 x 12 x 72"

**SEAT**

72"

3/4 x 2-1/2 x 70"

3/4 x 1-1/2 x 70"

3" BUTT HINGE

5-5/8"

3/4 x 5-3/8"

**FOLDED POSITION**

B

TURNBUTTON

TURN BUTTON

1-1/2 x 2-3/8 x 20-7/8"

**UNFOLDED POSITION**

1x4 NOTCHED STRETCHER

35-3/4"

TURN BUTTON

13/16 x 3-9/16" NOTCH

3/4 x 1-1/4" NOTCH

LEG

1x4 STRETCHER

3"

B

TURNBUTTON

LEG

1 x 2 x 8-1/4"

1/4 x 3/4" HINGE RABBET

3" BUTT HINGE

BUTT HINGE

1x4 HINGED BRACE

1x4

3/4" PLYWOOD TOP

35-3/4"

ROUTER OR SAW KERFS 4-1/2" APART

7" RAD.

29"

12"

14-3/4"

3/4" SQ. BLOCK

12"

LIFT-OFF BENCHTOP

TWO 3" BUTTS

8" RAD.

**END VIEW**

15-1/2"

8" RAD.

7" RAD.

3/4" EXTERIOR-GRADE PLYWOOD

15-1/8"

15-1/4"

30-1/2"

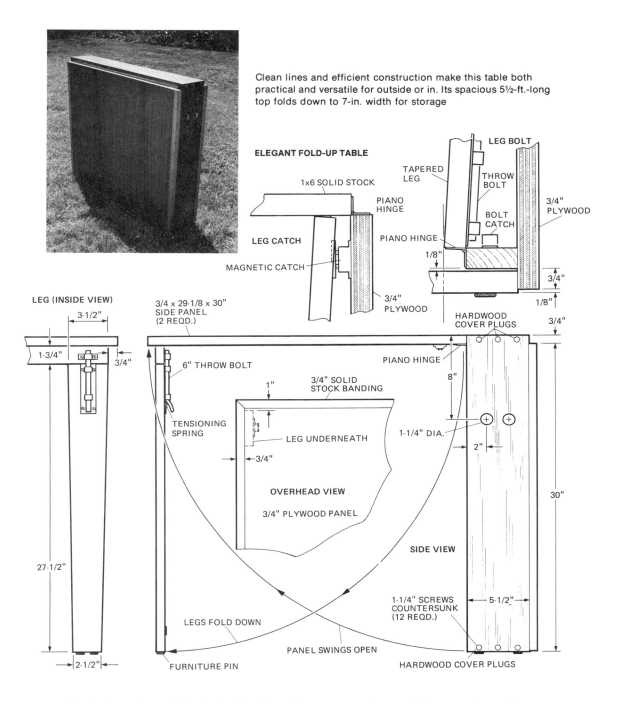

Clean lines and efficient construction make this table both practical and versatile for outside or in. Its spacious 5½-ft.-long top folds down to 7-in. width for storage

**ELEGANT FOLD-UP TABLE**

LEG BOLT

TAPERED LEG

THROW BOLT

BOLT CATCH

3/4" PLYWOOD

PIANO HINGE

1/8"

3/4"

1/8"

1x6 SOLID STOCK

PIANO HINGE

LEG CATCH

MAGNETIC CATCH

3/4" PLYWOOD

HARDWOOD COVER PLUGS

3/4"

LEG (INSIDE VIEW)

3/4 x 29-1/8 x 30" SIDE PANEL (2 REQD.)

PIANO HINGE

3-1/2"

1-3/4"

3/4"

6" THROW BOLT

8"

TENSIONING SPRING

1"

3/4" SOLID STOCK BANDING

LEG UNDERNEATH

1-1/4" DIA.

2"

3/4"

OVERHEAD VIEW

3/4" PLYWOOD PANEL

30"

27-1/2"

SIDE VIEW

LEGS FOLD DOWN

PANEL SWINGS OPEN

1-1/4" SCREWS COUNTERSUNK (12 REQD.)

5-1/2"

2-1/2"

FURNITURE PIN

HARDWOOD COVER PLUGS

a rich, dark tone) to a light birch. You'll need a sharp blade (carbide tipped is ideal) to cut the panels without damaging the edges. A plywood blade also will do the job nicely.

Assemble the center frame first. For good, tight construction, cut a ¼×¾-in. rabbet along the edges of the vertical center boards and lock in the horizontal members with glue and screws. Con-

trasting wood plugs are inserted into the countersunk holes. Let them extend ¹⁄₁₆ in. to assure a smooth, flush finish when you do the sanding. Furniture pins in the bottom of the legs help steady the completed table. We used teak oil for a lustrous finish. Whichever table you build, it will be there when you need it and fold out of the way when you don't.

# SHOP GUIDE

## CUSTOMARY TO METRIC (CONVERSION)

Conversion factors can be carried so far they become impractical. In cases below where an entry is exact it is followed by an asterisk (*). Where considerable rounding off has taken place, the entry is followed by a + or a − sign.

### Linear Measure

| inches | millimeters |
|---|---|
| 1/16 | 1.5875* |
| 1/8 | 3.2 |
| 3/16 | 4.8 |
| 1/4 | 6.35* |
| 5/16 | 7.9 |
| 3/8 | 9.5 |
| 7/16 | 11.1 |
| 1/2 | 12.7* |
| 9/16 | 14.3 |
| 5/8 | 15.9 |
| 11/16 | 17.5 |
| 3/4 | 19.05* |
| 13/16 | 20.6 |
| 7/8 | 22.2 |
| 15/16 | 23.8 |
| 1 | 25.4* |

| inches | centimeters |
|---|---|
| 1 | 2.54* |
| 2 | 5.1 |
| 3 | 7.6 |
| 4 | 10.2 |
| 5 | 12.7* |
| 6 | 15.2 |
| 7 | 17.8 |
| 8 | 20.3 |
| 9 | 22.9 |
| 10 | 25.4* |
| 11 | 27.9 |
| 12 | 30.5 |

| feet | centimeters | meters |
|---|---|---|
| 1 | 30.48* | .3048* |
| 2 | 61 | .61 |
| 3 | 91 | .91 |
| 4 | 122 | 1.22 |
| 5 | 152 | 1.52 |
| 6 | 183 | 1.83 |
| 7 | 213 | 2.13 |
| 8 | 244 | 2.44 |
| 9 | 274 | 2.74 |
| 10 | 305 | 3.05 |
| 50 | 1524* | 15.24* |
| 100 | 3048* | 30.48* |

1 yard = .9144* meters
1 rod = 5.0292* meters
1 mile = 1.6 kilometers
1 nautical mile = 1.852* kilometers

### Weights

| ounces | grams |
|---|---|
| 1 | 28.3 |
| 2 | 56.7 |
| 3 | 85 |
| 4 | 113 |
| 5 | 142 |
| 6 | 170 |
| 7 | 198 |
| 8 | 227 |
| 9 | 255 |
| 10 | 283 |
| 11 | 312 |
| 12 | 340 |
| 13 | 369 |
| 14 | 397 |
| 15 | 425 |
| 16 | 454 |

Formula (exact):
ounces × 28.349 523 125* = grams

| pounds | kilograms |
|---|---|
| 1 | .45 |
| 2 | .9 |
| 3 | 1.4 |
| 4 | 1.8 |
| 5 | 2.3 |
| 6 | 2.7 |
| 7 | 3.2 |
| 8 | 3.6 |
| 9 | 4.1 |
| 10 | 4.5 |

1 short ton (2000 lbs) = 907 kilograms (kg)
Formula (exact):
pounds × .453 592 37* = kilograms

### Fluid Measure

(Milliliters [ml] and cubic centimeters [cc] are equivalent, but it is customary to use milliliters for liquids.)

1 cu in = 16.39 ml
1 fl oz = 29.6 ml
1 cup = 237 ml
1 pint = 473 ml
1 quart = 946 ml
= .946 liters
1 gallon = 3785 ml
= 3.785 liters
Formula (exact):
fluid ounces × 29.573 529 562 5* = milliliters

### Volume

1 cu in = 16.39 cubic centimeters (cc)
1 cu ft = 28 316.7 cc
1 bushel = 35 239.1 cc
1 peck = 8 809.8 cc

### Area

1 sq in = 6.45 sq cm
1 sq ft = 929 sq cm
= .093 sq meters
1 sq yd = .84 sq meters
1 acre = 4 046.9 sq meters
= .404 7 hectares
1 sq mile = 2 589 988 sq meters
= 259 hectares
= 2.589 9 sq kilometers

### Miscellaneous

1 British thermal unit (Btu) (mean)
= 1 055.9 joules
1 horsepower = 745.7 watts
= .75 kilowatts
caliber (diameter of a firearm's bore in hundredths of an inch)
= .254 millimeters (mm)

1 atmosphere pressure = 101 325* pascals (newtons per sq meter)
1 pound per square inch (psi) = 6 895 pascals
1 pound per square foot = 47.9 pascals
1 knot = 1.85 kilometers per hour
1 mile per hour = 1.6093 kilometers per hour